DISCARDED

Daughter
of the House

Daughter
of the House

Evelyn Ames

HOUGHTON MIFFLIN COMPANY BOSTON
THE RIVERSIDE PRESS CAMBRIDGE

1 9 6 2

818
A

72754

For my brother, Harry,
and for Betsy

Part I

Prologue

AFTER three days which were very cold and dark for June, the city had wakened to a flawless morning. The sun, from the moment it rose beyond the Connecticut River, warmed housefronts and the eyelids of sleepers, set grass and leaves, wherever it touched them, to steaming. But on Forest Street, where the trees were so tall, the shrubbery old and thick, the great lawns and downstairs rooms of houses swam in a flickering, green-gold dusk until nearly nine o'clock. By that time many cars were parked along the street, their drivers having walked the two blocks south toward the factories or gone, in the opposite direction, to the shopping center on the avenue. Each year business penetrated the surrounding city more, yet here, with all that grass, that forest of leaves stirring and stretching and sighing, it still smelled like the country; people walking along were apt to raise their heads and breathe more deeply.

A few trucks came through, making early deliveries; laundry was hung out; at Number 59 a maid clipped the red setter puppy to his chain trolley and left him to bark. An unexceptional if perfect summer morning it seemed, yet if you looked more closely it wasn't, quite; the street was not as it usually was. In front of one of its finest houses, for instance, fresh depressions in the ground — like new graves — showed where shrubs had been dug up and not replaced, and the grass needed trimming. Number 73, next to Dr. Porter's, had not only been vacated but somebody had boarded up the windows since yesterday and nailed a "No Trespassing — Police take notice" sign onto the maple out front where — against the craggy bark of that soaring trunk — it looked a trifle absurd and temporary. At the end house on the lane running down toward the river, a moving van almost as large as the house itself was backed up to the front porch and furniture was being passed out of one open maw and into another — the moving men's loud banter silencing the birds — sending them, agitated, a few trees away. The end had begun.

Another house that was nearly empty was Number 55, halfway between the avenue and where Hawthorn crossed Forest. The largest house on the street, and set in the most land, it was ornately shingled and stained a dark brown that had deepened in the shade to the color of a copper beech, faded in the sun to cinnamon. It stood endwise to the street, separated from it by a bank of eight-foot high azaleas and by a thick grove of Japanese cedars three times as tall. Other sides were planted with rhododendrons and laurel or shaded by enormous trees, so that only from the south, across a wide lawn, could you see its irregular shape — all gables and bays and dormers — its windows set into mullions the color of thick cream.

There were lots of windows. On the north stair landing they were tall and narrow with rounded tops; there was also one of stained glass — all lumpy pink fish scales with blue whirligigs, like waves, along the bottom — but most of them had one very wide pane of glass in the bottom half and a mass of little diamond-shaped ones, like an English cottage, above.

Inside the house, this morning, every room was empty except for a whirl of debris — as though a hurricane had come through; light fixtures, half ripped out, hung by their wires; the door to the wine cellar stood ajar. All sorts of doors that used to be kept closed, even locked, were open now, their dozens of keys laid on the mantel of the largest bedroom, while the front door of two-inch oak stood furthest open of all letting in the wind. Oddly enough, neither the emptiness nor the air blowing through had removed the house's smell — a complex unidentifiable smell, not musty like some old houses, nor waxy and polishy, but spicy, rather, and unfamiliar. It had in it something of the Far East.

In the front hall, where the smell was strongest and the stairs swept out into widening curves at the bottom, stood a round-topped trunk fastened with straps and, on one end, the sticker of a hotel in Port Said. Its destination now was a boys' boarding school; its contents — fancy dress costumes: Turkish and Chinese and Greek; a homemade one of a cave man with a burlap, paper-stuffed club, and one of a teddy bear with a huge papier-mâché head which its owner once wore while driving to a party with the top of his car down.

Stripped and bare, the interior showed how spacious the

house was, what privacy and wide views of outdoors it had given its inhabitants. They were all that was left now of its unusual and rich atmosphere — one not created by valuable furnishings for it had had quite a hodgepodge of these, but by the kinds of lives it had sheltered and what had been produced, or collected, in the living of them. Until the last owner was moved out and the auction held, every room had been crammed full. Three generations had lived here — people who went around the world and brought things home; wrote books and painted and played musical instruments; acted (one professionally) and staged plays; gave enormous parties and developed their own photographs; made, for a time, their own wine. The activities of the last owner alone would have filled most ordinary houses and everything added together made a sort of wine: pressed down and fermented, having its own particular flavor, some of it clouded and gone to vinegar. Its bouquet was derived from the occupants themselves: what they were and did in the house, what life did to them.

In an upstairs window seat, only a few yards away from the grey pillars of trees, one of these occupants was sitting with a notebook in her lap, writing. A middle-aged woman with greying hair, she was the daughter of the house; for months she had been coming from her own home, three hours away, to empty this one and today her work would be finished. She was quite accustomed by now (or so she thought) to the sensation of meeting herself as the child who had grown up in these walls: at any moment it might happen — the look of a particular picture, turning up some object she had not seen for decades among the thousands and thousands of things she had had to scrutinize and decide about, and there she would be — face to face with that earlier self, each confronting the other with a mixture of familiarity and astonishment — an interested and startled "so this is you!"

This morning — because it was the last morning and everything gone from the house but herself and that other self — the encounter was so sharp it was almost of the senses. One of life's circles had closed, and the child, begging her mother "Can't I have a place somewhere alone and quiet to write in, *please?*" had found it at last in fantastic acute reality. Only reality is as fantastic as this (she thought): here, just when everything is about to end — utterly — I am sitting undisturbed and unpressed, the house around me and I looking out from this window on the world into a grove I love, its breath blowing in through the screen onto my skin. I am free to write. I've a place to write from. It's what I always used to dream of having so that now, for the first time, it is as though I *were* that child. How odd! As though all along I had been my own ghost . . .

A bird whizzed past her at eye level, with a f-ft sound and a flash of blue. Out of sight it cried. Oh no, she almost protested aloud, laying down her pencil: blue jays do that in *autumn!* And now footsteps were approaching along the upstairs hall, resounding and echoing in the emptiness: she had forgotten about the man who had been working in the house all night — collecting rubbish, taking out shelves. There he stood, behind him the exposed layers of ancient wallpapers where, before, there had been nothing but

books, green light from the stair landing scooping deep
shadows in his gaunt face. He glanced at where the book-
shelves had been, at the dangling fixtures, and shook his
head.

"Shame — nice house like this."

"Yes, it is."

"If you need anything done, I'm here. Just holler."

"Thank you, I will. What did you say your name was?"

"Jo."

"What's your regular work, Jo?"

"Freight-handling. Down to the yards. I'm a night
freight handler."

"Oh." She couldn't think of anything else to say, but
with her train of thought broken into, something caught
her attention. He could help her, she told him; there were
some last things to go into her car.

Between them, in silence, they carried out and packed
some articles the auctioneer had put to one side, things she
had not yet been able to part with or decide what to do
about. Here was the life mask of her brother (what had
become of that sculptress he loved so?) and the box of her
father's academic hoods; there were three of her dolls; a
package of love letters; a locked tin box, contents unknown, for which she might possibly have the key at home.
Beside some teacups (forgotten last time) she propped the
house number, taken off its tree: a glass sign with two large
fives beginning to lose their gold paint. She put it all into
the luggage compartment along with her own suitcase.
Inside the car Jo was standing pictures, separating them
with pieces of cloth.

"Oh, goodness," she said, recognizing the brocade curtains from the smoking room, "let's use something else for that."

He stopped, puzzled, the gold-shot red material clutching at his rough fingers.

"These would be wonderful for costumes," she told him, and with his help opened the trunk in the hall and laid the beautiful stuff on top. Buckling the straps once more, he smiled apologetically.

"You see, I wouldn't know about something like that." He looked at her sharply. "Must hurt, don't it? Giving up all these things?" She nodded. "What I want to know," he went on, "is why do they pick a place like *this?*"

A good many people wanted to know, especially — and bitterly — the families in the ten other houses marked for demolition. In the architects' offices last plans were being drawn up; the wrecking cranes and bulldozers would soon come clanking in and what was once the heart of a colony called Nook Farm, created by a number of exceptional families, would become the new High School and the approaches to a new East-West thruway. In place of these old houses — some, like this one, great homely arks of the nineteenth century, others with beautiful, restrained exteriors, but all of them rich with the collected past — instead of the quiet lawns and great trees, there would be a one story, wide-spread building; new, low planting; macadam parking areas glittering with gaily colored cars. Sun would pour in upon the thousands of students as it never could into these shaded old mansions, embroidered with vines, their rooms, in summer, like rooms under sea. No one would ever go up or down stairs any more, or sit in window seats part-way up trees, or look out from third floor gables into caves of foliage, at the eye of a squirrel, into a nest full of eggs . . .

She went back upstairs, to the empty guest room and her seat in the trees. How differently life would go on, she thought, in the old space, the new frame! All that river of energy arriving in torrents each morning and sorting itself into different streams! All that crowd life — dammed up, compressed into classrooms — where once a small boy had had chicken pox in a cheerful, messy bedroom — bed covered with toys, the first narcissus on too tall stems reaching for the window; a husband and wife had come home after a party, gone into their room and closed the door. In one way the individual lives of eleven families shrank down to nothing in comparison; in another, they grew to terrible and fascinating intensity.

And what of the contents of the houses, like layers of iridescence inside these old shells (or like grains of sand and bits of beach straw) — what of them? Records of how the houses used to look and what was in them would be available to scholars; many things would be moved into other houses; the rest would be scattered all over: into antique shops, institutions; broken up and burned on the city dump. It is what happens when houses are destroyed, while the secrets — what really matters — trickle on, diluted, in the memories and anecdotes of descendants: "Don't you remember? Father said it belonged to that great-great-grandfather — the one who died of a slave's bite" — either that or they go down with the house, as people's secrets go into the grave. For a house, too, is something of an organism — ingesting, secreting, enduring, excreting and always storing, storing, storing away.

What would her father say, if he knew? He was still alive when he left the house for the last time, though his mind was in some other world. Sometimes it was hunting deer in Sherwood Forest, with a longbow, the next moment it was at the opera, in Paris (are the seats all right? can you see?). All the boundaries were gone, both in space and time: the dead were as present as the living, but neither was there an actual present and so any knowledge of what his lifelong home was to become.

Hartford High! How often, how lovingly he spoke of it! No subsequent tributes or honorary degrees meant more to him than the High School's diploma and the Commencement program listing him as valedictorian. What would he say? And her mother — born in another country; all her later years a sad oscillation between her native home and this into which she put her heart and in which a heart attack finally killed her? And their long-dead neighbor, the actor Will Gillette, so astringent and urbane and derangingly handsome — whose house, along with the barn that hid runaway slaves on the way to Canada — was one of the eleven? And, on the other side of Number 55, Charles Dudley Warner of the encyclopedic, whimsical mind, the long, aristocratic hands? Most startling of all to contemplate, what would issue from under the white tussock of Mark Twain's moustache — Mark Twain, whose house, less than a football field away, was being preserved? Or *his* neighbor, Harriet Beecher Stowe, whose house was

also to be spared, though none of the charming conservatories she had designed for her friends and neighbors up
and down the street . . .

Oh, there were many ghosts about this morning, those of
the living as well as the dead, and all of them more real to
her up in her window seat than that red setter puppy yap-
ping and yanking at the end of his chain, or the neighbors'
little redheaded boy out on the lawn, furiously explaining
something to his younger sister — his thin, intense figure in
its faded blue jeans aggressively facing her round and stubborn one. Unseen by either of them, at the foot of a nearby
oak a hundred feet tall, two little girls in smocked dresses, a
boy in knickers, were building houses among the tree's
roots. The blond one ran back and forth from the driveway with pebbles which the dark one laid as steppingstones in the moss and edged with the heads of dandelions.
Clouds of bluets in full flower appeared to drift over the
grass around them, moving and whitening in the breeze
that lifted the hems of the girls' dresses. All three children
almost stood on their heads in the intense labor of balanc-
ing roofs of twigs and bark between the flying buttresses of
the tree's base, making fences around miniature gardens.
"*My* way's better than *that!*" "Look, Tibbie, watch me!"
How they competed! Or else drifted off into gentle canti-
cles in praise of their own work. They were the *real* children — at least half of life unrolled for them by now, its
memories completed. The two in blue jeans — everything
ahead of them, untried, unloved, ungrieved — they seemed,
this morning, more like ghosts . . .

A fresh breath from outdoors brought back the present:

fragrant, moist, full of motion — leaves lifting and turning
in a slow dance, disclosing before they sighed downward
again glimpses of the other houses, of the street — under a
long branch — where a car, passing, made a thrrrrumppp
as its wheels dropped over a bump . . . Feel everything
here around you, just as it is, she commanded herself; recall
all you know about it: next year it won't be here. She
picked up her notebook again and began to write.

Forest Street had changed remarkably little in appearance since it was originally colonized by John Hooker,
descendant of the founder of Connecticut and husband of
one of the fabulous Beechers. Lyman Beecher, the great
divine, had had thirteen children of whom eight achieved
fame: five preachers, an educator, a suffragist, and Harriet,
the author of *Uncle Tom's Cabin*. Three of them made
their homes at Nook Farm and it was they who set the tone
of the whole community; from the day they moved in, it
was a place where religion and intellectuality flourished, in
an atmosphere of the greatest congeniality. Each family
kept open house to the others and there were evenings of
such lively exchange that one foreign visitor, who later
visited Dean Howells and dined with Longfellow, wrote
home that he found Cambridge "very pale and colorless"
by comparison. There were evenings of parlor games and
large family picnics; the wives often lunched together,
walking to each other's houses across lawns and gardens
which connected rather than separated them.
A few things looked different now: the surface of the
street was macadam; a small apartment building replaced

the Hooker house and shortly after the First World War two new houses had gone up across from Number 55. They ruined the street's one coasting hill, being placed as they were just where the children ran with their sleds for the take-off, at the foot of a great old oak. The tree had to go. When the children came home after school to find it on the ground, its limbs sawed off, they held a memorial service; one of them played Taps, on a harmonica. (Hadn't she recited "The Highwayman," her favorite poem?) The street, until sometime in the twenties, was like any country road of that day. Summers, it raised clouds of dust that hung in the air long after an automobile had passed and powdered every leaf with grit. In the spring it grew two uneven pairs of ruts in the mud, which crossed each other here and there or turned into pits where a wheel had been mired and violently tried to spin its way out. (What an agonized snarl it made — almost more dreadful than sirens for that terrible, repeated sound of struggle, defeat, struggle, defeat!) Winters, after a succession of snowstorms, icestorms, thaws and freezes, it became so impassable that people locked their cars into the garages until spring.

Wagons, or sleighs, brought what was needed: the milkwagon, whose lantern drew slowly evolving designs of light across darkened ceilings; the great drays, drawn by Percherons or Belgian Greys, which delivered coal and wood; the covered Express Wagon which carried away all the trunks required at summer cottages, or on trips to Europe. The children came to know the different horses and to have favorites to whom they slipped lumps of sugar as the ani-

mals stood waiting, heads hanging down. One horse and
carriage with which they were all familiar was the one that
belonged to "old Dr. Porter" (was he always old?), a
pinched and grey and salty little man who lived next to the
Stowes in an austere, grey house that bulged toward the
street into one of his neighbor's original conservatories.
All winter luminous colors hovered like tropical fish inside
the steamy windows and passers-by could vaguely make
out Mrs. Porter, watering, pruning, repotting. Dr. Porter's
horse was, like his master, patient and slow. He even
seemed wise, and one little boy's happiest moment was
when the horse, tied up and waiting outside a neighbor's
house, turned to him and whinnied. "I saw Dr. Porter's
horse," he ran in and told his mother, "and he knew me!
How did he recognize me, Mother, how?"

Though the street had been resurfaced, the sidewalks
were still the same. They were unusual — the flagstones
very large and in places so rough that puddles stayed in
them long after a rain; and there were some — extremely
pale grey, that were so full of mica they looked like moon-
lit water and even on the darkest day were a mass of sparkles. For roller-skating they were treacherous. When the
electrical-equipment factory was built on Hawthorn
Street, the children raced there: on the new cement walks
they could coast down one hill and up another with the
barest perceptible rhythmical clack at each joint, yet they
always returned to the roughness of the beautiful stones
outside their houses. It shook their teeth and eyeballs and
tickled their bones and often bloodied their knees, yet they
loved it for the wonderful roar it made under their skates,

the spouts of water its puddles shot out from their wheels.

The same street and the same houses, set in their banks of rhododendron and falls of forsythia. The same trees, only larger, fuller, more completely themselves, more utterly melancholy. (Why? Was it the sound of so much foliage, like the sound of the sea? Or was it that there was so much more and bigger mortality, so that the prospect of its loss was that much worse — as a dead horse seems many times more terrible than a dead cat?) No — almost nothing had changed. It was an even quieter, gentler oasis for what had happened beyond it.

It even sounded very nearly the same — the noise of the city, like a great humming, all around; above this, and nearer, a wood thrush's chords, the self-interrupted rhapsodies of orioles, the mourning of doves. And, woven through everything, the steady undertone, the day-long accompaniment of the machine presses in the factory half a mile away. Their hammering was irregular: bang, bang; bang-bang-bang; bang. Oh dear, that *noise*, one said to oneself, sitting outdoors, especially when the wind was in the south; what a pity, thought the out-of-town visitor, admiring the iris garden, watching the copper beech slowly turning its burnished surfaces in a breeze. Yet it was that noise that gave the gardens and the woods beyond their delicious sense of sanctuary: out *there* might be machines, industry, the world; here was this garden, this dale carpeted with trillium and Jack-in-the-pulpit, overarched by hundred-foot trees.

At night, in bed, one heard the trains come through: the loud stutter of Diesels, now, with their complaining bleat, and because the subsoil was like jelly and the tracks were down at the end of the street, the houses shook as if in an earthquake, pictures rattled on the walls. Waking in the early morning it was the machine presses one listened for first: they were the heartbeat of the day. Had they started yet? If so, it was after seven.

It was the trees that had changed most, the gardens and woods that were larger, deeper, greener, particularly down by the river where the lawns ended and the land dropped steeply away. Here was a four- or five-acre stand of forest with oaks and beeches as stately and monumental as any in England, at their feet huge ferns and — in the clearings — breast-high grass that squeaked with juice. Above one of these clearings, its foundations all but drowned in sprays of blackberry and overgrown mock orange, stood the "slave barn." After runaway slaves it housed horses, until a fire burned them up one terrible night in the twenties when the snow lay so deep the engines couldn't get through. (Next day she and the other little girl from under the tree spent hours poking about in the cold, charred ruins — breathing in the wet stench, nerving themselves to look at unimagined horrors — an adventure that had ended, for her, in a shaking chill and a fever which burned for a week: it was the winter of the Spanish flu.) Now, instead of horses, the barn housed cars, and soon there would be nothing at all — not even the echoes of whinnying screams — for don't ghosts need a shell, as sound requires an ear?

Close to the river — a small, muddy tributary of the Connecticut — it was mosquitoey and clouds of little flies danced above the heavy-headed weeds. Where, in her childhood, it had been almost wild woods, a network of paths wound along the riverbanks and up the sides of the ravine — the more traveled ones worn bare and strewn with crumpled cigarette and chewing-gum wrappers, bright slivers of cellophane. Others, little more than dog paths, led to places where the slope was gentle enough for grass to grow — pale grass as soft as newly washed hair, pressed down here and there by people's weight.

Above this, at the very edge of the high land, stood the Warner house — three and a half stories of brick with a hip roof of slate. On the top floor you were so high you looked out over the tops of the tallest trees, all the way to Talcott Mountain, while the view down to the forest floor was quite dizzying. It was a cozy house, every room with its fireplace and at least one deep, windowed alcove where the windows were grouped together and had a wide sill for plants. It was a house (like this one, like Number 55) filled with great richness . . .

Charles Dudley Warner had not only been loved by everyone in town but as editor of the paper, author and wit, he was known all over the country. Mark Twain was one of his closest friends and often, after dinner, the Clemenses walked over for talk and whist, staying until very late. Other neighbors dropped in and a succession of writers — all protégés at one time or another — Sarah Orne Jewett, Frances Hodgson Burnett, Bret Harte, Joel Chandler Harris — came to visit, to participate in the Nook Farm life, to find refreshment.

There had been no Warner children; Susan, who played the piano with almost professional skill, had mothered young musicians and entertained famous ones at morning musicales which filled every cranny of the downstairs rooms with Hartford's ladies. (She remembered attending these as the only child present, invited — and excused from school — because she was supposed to have musical talent. All those waves of matronly bosoms that hemmed her in, perched on a creaky folding chair! The syrupy sweetness of the women! But Mrs. Warner, with her fine, aquiline nose and brisk manner, was from another world altogether, as was the passion of music that fountained upward and broke against the walls. How had they existed together? In the same room?)

The house had never lost its aliveness, some innate energy transfusing whoever lived in it. Its present, final owners (whom she often visited now) were musicians too: the vacuum cleaner might be roaring in one room but violin notes were doing acrobatics in the next; in the evening quartets made music together. Everywhere was the clutter of life being lived, hard: sheets of music, pictures crayoned by children, clothes, letters, foamed up in joyous confusion; violins lay where they were put down at the ring of a telephone, a petticoat flounced up like a can-can dancer from the back of a chair. And in the middle of all the seethe and hubbub which the house generously absorbed, the children's mother, a lock of hair escaping its knot, her face flushed, listened to a screaming younger sister. "Yes, yes, Annie, I *know* it's awful. Now tell me, and tell the truth: did you hit him first?" Even on a February day, when trees dripped and dripped, blackening the bark in long streaks, leaving dirty pits in the snow, when gutters and drains made a noise of far-off streams, the house, inside, was filled with the color and tangle and urgency of an orchard in spring.

Behind it stood a brown-painted barn, back to back with Mark Twain's barn, and then *his* house — a wonderful great extravaganza of brick, all zigzagged with patterns and topped by a slate roof as diamond-backed as a rattlesnake's skin. Steeply pointed gables sheltered odd little balconies and Mrs. Stowe's finest and largest conservatory fanned out under its half-cone of roof. Beside it, the main, flat-roofed porch extended southward, riding the crest of the ridge like the pilot house of a Mississippi river steamboat.

Here Samuel Clemens spent the happiest, and the saddest, days of his life. He wrote *Tom Sawyer* and *Huckleberry Finn* there, *A Connecticut Yankee* and *The Prince and the Pauper* — often reading chapters aloud as he finished them to his wife and daughters and neighbors. He took twenty-mile walks with his closest, most irreverent friend, the Reverend Joe Twitchell, and came home to sit with him for more talk by the fire. He entertained handsomely and with delight. (In what had once been the Clemens children's schoolroom, on the top floor, she had first gone to school. Would it ever leave her, the horror of one particular morning? At recess, on the porch, her friends had tried to string her up by the lines that rolled and unrolled the awning: with the cord in a slipknot around her neck, the teacher too busy to notice, they had very nearly succeeded. What had she done? No one remembered.)

The house was a museum now, everything in it arranged as if Samuel Clemens and his family still lived there. The

table was set for dinner; fresh towels hung over the enormous bathtub in its mahogany frame. In the conservatory
a cockateel and a budgerigar tried to outchatter the splash
of water over a marble nymph; and in the children's
room — how sad it was! — a little plaid and ruffled taffeta
dress hung on a clothestree ready to be put on; a doll stared
intently from its carriage. There, too, in the guest room off
the conservatory, stood the great black walnut bed in
which Mark's daughter Susie died of meningitis while her
parents were abroad, before they could get home to her.
The bed was all made up, pillows in their ruched and
ruffled "shams," the mattress covered with a crocheted
spread. How empty it looked; how it echoed Mark Twain's
recurrent saying: "Nook Farm is no longer in Hartford, but
in the city of Heartbreak." (Be quiet, birds! Let the bed
speak . . .)

The same street, the same houses; their present occupants even saw life much as their predecessors did. It was
the city that was no longer the same — the city everywhere
which was turning all Nook Farms, all Forest Streets, into
backwaters. On a June evening now, teen-agers from
"town" made the woods their own, dropping their bicycles
on the lawns, shouting with fun as they walked a fallen
tree trunk or played Tarzan. The violinist, a lawyer by
profession, a gentle man by nature, left them alone even
though it meant taking after-dinner coffee on the terrace
to raucous shouts. But last night, when she was there, he
had stepped in.

"None of that!" he shouted down the ravine, "no fighting, or I call the cops!"

Two girls with kerchiefed heads and babies on their

arms stood at the top of the slope where the earth was trampled bare; they stared at him. Down in the shadows came the flare of a match. At this he called the boys up to him and they came, reluctantly, and stood leaning on their bikes.

"Look, boys, there can't be any smoking. The woods are too dry. That's just *out*, see?"

"Only one of us was smoking."

"One's enough to start a fire."

No one moved.

"Why don't you go over to Pope's Park? It's only half a mile from here and you can do as you like there."

"We can't. The cops say get out wise guys."

"Why 'wise guys'?"

"Dunno. That's what they call us."

Still no one moved, though the young mothers, unnoticed, had slipped away. One leg across the bar of their bicycles, they stood poised for flight, faces truculent, the dark-skinned, curly-haired leader of the group with hostility flashing from flinty eyes. The youngest and smallest appeared to weigh what was being said: he looked troubled. Somebody muttered — a sound like a growl.

"All right!" came the reply, angered for the first time. "That's enough! This is off bounds, and if I catch you here again, I'll call the cops!"

"C'mon! Get the hell out!" yelled the leader, like a battle cry, and gravel spurted up behind their departing wheels . . .

The main stream was breaking through as it inevitably does. (Did Cicero chase boys from the foot of *his* garden?) Eventually the single houseowner, however gentle and civilized, is outweighed, outrushed: he must move out of the path of the flood or be drowned.

The owners of the Warner house, as of most of the others, were moving to higher land, taking as much of their former life with them as they possibly could: seeds and offshoots of the house here — its warm vitality and flowering — were sure to flourish there. And the Mark Twain house was safe — as the fern buried by time is safe, every least frond recorded in stone, the delicate greenness gone. But of *this* house, the Perkins house, nothing would remain but what a few people remembered of it.

1

SHE DID NOT hear him come up behind her; suddenly an arm was around her waist and she was being spun around.

"Henry, look out! You'll muss me all up!" yet she giggled with pleasure just the same, tucking in her chin like a very young, very coquettish girl.

"You look wonderful, Mother!" he was saying, holding her off to look at her, "prettiest girl in town!"

She beamed at him: such a *straight* young man — not tall, but with a marvelous, proud way of carrying his head; a very straightforward look; the shiniest, most contagious smile.

Right behind him stood Edward, more tentative and dreamy-eyed than his brother, his features very fine-drawn, his blond hair very wavy. He kissed his mother shyly, and a laugh rather like her own expressed what he could not, or perhaps preferred not to say.

Henry consulted his watch: yes there was time. "I've a surprise for you," he said, darting off toward the dining room.

Mary Perkins was giving a dance to celebrate the finishing of the new house, and Henry's graduating, with honors, from Yale. She adored giving parties; in fact she adored giving: it was the role life had given her and which she played with such zest, such charm that it became a virtue. (Sometimes, when she gave on her terms, insistently, self-consciously, it was also her vice. "No, my dear," she would say to the embarrassed recipient of an exaggerated, even unwanted gift or favor, "I *want* you to have it; it is my *pleasure*.")

The party, this evening late in June, would give many people pleasure — over two hundred in fact. New neighbors who were coming to pay their respects; old friends from Prospect Street who were driving the two miles out into the country to have a look at the new house; her sons' friends who were coming for the dancing and refreshments.

The day had been sultry and miserable with occasional growls of thunder, but between seven and eight in the evening a heavy shower freshened the air, leaving it saturated with the odors of earth and leaves and grass. The hostess, on her way downstairs, paused on the landing to look out at the new young laurels and rhododendrons which had just been put in around the entrance. They had had a good watering, she saw: their leaves glittered like looking glasses and large drops rolled off them into the chocolate-rich earth.

She went on down, her new lilac taffeta crackling and swishing, its silent reflection slowly descending across the hall mirror. A little pigeon of a woman: sleek and plump and high-chested; from waist to floor all draped and upholstered and bustled in the fin de siècle fashion so that even her own sons hadn't known till their mid-teens that their mother was, like themselves, bifurcated. She felt very festive not to be wearing black, to have bare shoulders. With a pang that stabbed her much less often now, she longed for her husband.

Walking slowly through the downstairs rooms, trying to see them through his, and her guests', eyes, she thought how he would have approved of this. Prospect Street was no longer what it had been: rowdies stole fruit from their trees and wakened them at all hours of the night with their ill-bred behavior and loud talk, while the house itself — what with her own parties and now the boys grown up and bringing home their friends — was entirely too small. She had been quite right to build this house; it was the beginning of a new life for them.

How fresh and handsome it all was: there was even a fragrance of new wood still in the air! The pale, hardwood floors glistened as the ones in the old house never did — reflecting the light from lamps and chandeliers. The lights themselves, inside their shades of iridescent apricot or green glass, hung in clusters from their brass stems. Steel engravings in wide oak frames, oil paintings in ornate gold ones covered the walls. The doorways were hung with new velvet portieres.

In the dining room, where white-covered tables were crowded with food and a coffee samovar strutted like a silver turkey among its flock of cups, two maids stood whispering together; the longed-for breeze moved the curtains inside their wide windows. Very sweetly and de-

murely, as though it were an unusual favor, Mary Perkins
asked the maids to make sure all the downstairs windows
were open. In the reception room, between this and the
living room, extra sofas and chairs brought in for the
evening from other rooms waited in a variety of poses and
shapes — padded or bony, curved or straight — the arched
necks of two gilded swans forming the arms of the sofa
where she would stand and receive. On the porch beyond, hurricane lamps set at formal intervals, each one a
small constellation of images and reflections around its
central flame, made a bridge between the lighted house
and the darkening lawn.

She went on into the living room. Emptied for dancing,
it looked larger than usual and she knew again how right
she had been about its dimensions as about the size of the
whole house. The Boston architects had been uneasy: was
she sure that a lady in her position, widowed, two grown
sons, wanted all that space? Yes, she had replied firmly,
she did. "I want large reception rooms, with sliding doors
between them so that I can cut them off from one another
and give *two* parties of a hundred at once if I care to."

She looked into the smoking room, where the orchestra
was to sit: she *hoped* the gentlemen would take the hint and
save their cigars for outdoors! Small palm trees, borrowed
from the Stowes' conservatory and placed around the musicians' chairs and music stands, made a sort of bower.
The effect was pretty but she was sorry it screened the
smoking-room mantel: such a miracle of oak carving — all
those garlands and clusters of grapes surrounding the family coat of arms, and — standing on either side of it — the

two life-sized herons with trailing crests. It was, she thought, the finest thing in the house, and looking at it, she gave a little low, gurgling chuckle. The house, the dance — oh it was all unbelievable!

She had not always been in this position to give and life had taken much away from her. All through her childhood in a country village in Massachusetts, nothing particular had ever happened except the loss of one baby brother and sister after another until finally only Will was left, and he so much younger he was more like her child than her brother. It had been very lonely. But the summer she was eighteen she was appointed village postmistress, and one by one as they came to pick up their mail, she met the different members of a wonderful family vacationing up the road: five redheaded, excitable children, their scholarly parents. They loved Mary: in the fall they took her back to the city with them where she attended a young ladies' seminary and helped, afternoons and evenings, with the children. One night when she came down to dinner there stood in the parlor a romantic, delicate-looking man — older, oh much older than herself — with a shock of blond hair and the gentlest of expressions. "Mary," she heard, "this is our cousin, Edward Perkins." He was the cousin no one in the family thought would get married: rheumatic fever had left him with such a weak heart he had had to pay a substitute to fight for him in the Civil War; he was painfully shy and reserved. But Mary's freshness and gaiety broke through to him; within a year they were married and the year after became the parents of a son, Henry — the one who was being honored tonight.

And now Henry had returned with his "surprise" —
was walking toward her with a bottle of champagne, a
little tray with three glasses. Behind him, she saw, the
musicians were arriving; the house after its lull of waiting,
of excitement suppressed, was full of stir. But no guests
had as yet come, and Henry swept his mother and brother
off to a couch in the reception room where the three of
them held their own little celebration together: a young
woman with two suitors, you would have thought, to look
at them. The festivities had begun.

Once under way, the party moved with its own life, to
its own crescendos, almost as though the young people so
energetically doing waltzes and polkas, the older people
conversing and circulating through the house, the servants
passing things, no longer obeyed their own wills. Even
the musicians, reading their notes with difficulty in the
dimly lit smoking room, did not quite seem to be calling
the tune. Some other music was prompting all that gaiety,
the elegance with which compliments were exchanged,
the interest guests showed. Was it entirely the new house
— the sense of excitement over something completed
(which was also just beginning)? Or wasn't it, too, the
realization that with Henry's graduation from college the
whole family picture had now subtly and importantly
changed?

Over and over during the evening — which went so fast,
flushing cheeks as though with wind, spinning shimmering
flirtations, generating plans for future meetings — over and
over Mary Perkins reflected on this landmark in hers and

her son's life. Once more there was a man in the house; there was a male head of the family.

There he was, sweeping past her with coattails swinging, his mouth — under the reddish blond moustache — parted in a smile. At something his partner said, he threw his head back in a loud laugh. He was dancing, she saw to her distaste, with that Sue Campbell; pretty little thing with all those bouncing curls and deep dimples, but quite common, really: they had had an argument about inviting her. Sue acted entirely too knowing: Mary Perkins wouldn't be surprised if she *did* know . . . well, everything. Still, both sons seemed attracted to her and she had better make up her mind to the fact that they were young men now, and anything could happen. As for her, she'd done her best with them; yet how was it possible: childhood went so *fast!* Henry had only just been a baby!

She remembered his christening — wrapping him, for good luck, in her own blue-embroidered flannel petticoat which she had worn on her wedding day — and how, as his godmother approached the font with him, a fold of the petticoat caught on a corner of the open coffin beside them. Inside the coffin lay the infant's grandfather, for whom he was to be named, his white hair shiny as the satin pillow under it, the two long, Lincolnesque furrows of the cheeks transformed by death from sternness to majesty. All of Hartford (that counted) was there in the church, for the dead man, who had worked since childhood to help support his parents and brothers and sisters, had died president of the city's largest bank; no one in town was more respected. "Henry Augustus Perkins, I

baptize thee in the name of the Father, the Son . . ."
There were several sharp intakes of breath; she tightened
the hold of her hand linked with her husband's, increasing the pound of their combined pulses . . .

He had been six months old that July morning; barely
three months later he began to walk. His father, thinking
it bad for him, kept pushing him down but he kept getting
up again.

He had talked early, too: "Book, book" he had said,
several times over, leaning excitedly forward in his high
chair toward the book she was reading as she sat with
him. Book, indeed! There couldn't be a young man to
whom books meant more, whose mind was so avid, who
had such a beautiful, agile memory. Well, there would be
books enough in *this* house!

Two years later Edward was born, nearly died of cholera
infantum, and the boys' father did die, leaving Mary and
her two small sons a town house and a moderate fortune.

She had not married again. For many years ill health
was her second husband, keeping her months at a time in
her ornate black walnut bed. There, surrounded by books
and flowers, her pretty hair piled in a waterfall of curls, she
created a pleasant and luxurious life for herself. Friends
came for tea and whist; she engaged tutors to teach her
and the children languages; she administered a wide net of
personal philanthropies, giving work or assistance to a
German wood carver here, a retired schoolteacher there.
But every day, no matter what else she did, she devoted
hours to Henry and Edward — reading aloud to them and
playing games with them, getting them to recite poems

to her and to act charades. At night, in bed, they heard her singing, accompanying herself on the guitar. Every day, too, she talked to them about their father whom they couldn't remember: how good and how pure he had been; how they must pray to be like him. She gave each of them a little book about him which his best friend wrote and had had privately printed after Edward Perkins' death. Twenty-six times in its pages, Edward was spoken of as "pure" or "of utmost purity."

If the boys were deprived of their father and of a natural boyhood they had a surfeit of privilege and security and mothering. Their mother! She dispensed such charm and sweetness, presents and parties, that they prized every moment in her room, at her bedside — they became attentive and chivalrous as lovers. What could be more wonderful than coming in to that smiling, flowery presence who, unlike other boys' mothers, was always there, in the same place, always ready to put work aside, and even dismiss the caller ("darling Sylvia — you will forgive me?") in order to listen to their latest, least adventure? And these she was determined they should have, so that summers, when she was not well enough, she sent them away to the mountains or the seashore, in the care of their Irish nursemaid and a Mrs. Mayer — another widowed lady — who gave them their lessons. Winters, too, were often spent away — at Aiken and Augusta, Nassau, Washington, always in search of their mother's health, the boys being tutored and not attending school, Henry avidly learning whatever came his way.

She finally got better and the summer Henry was thirteen

they made their first of many trips to Europe. *La Gascoigne* used sails as well as steam and each morning the boys rushed out on deck to see which way the yards were hauled, the squaresails set. Somewhere in the hold their trunks were piled up, filled not only with all the clothes needed for a summer abroad, but the many appurtenances of travel: folding spirit lamps, padded bottle cases, traveling flasks and pillows and bookbags. On the stern deck, out of the strong wind, their mother sat rolled up in steamer-rugs, her head wrapped in a cloud of grey chiffon, writing innumerable letters, which, as they were finished, she tucked into pockets of her voluminous writing-case for mailing at Le Havre. Under the rugs, the long wool skirt, silk petticoat, flannel petticoat — just outside the Jaeger wool union suit (it was still early May) was fastened the elaborately harnessed money belt in which the money for the trip made a thick and reassuring package. Small bills and Baedekers were in her handbag, but sometimes, in emergencies, it would be necessary to retreat behind the palms in a hotel lobby in order to extricate enough cash to pay the bill. Elsewhere on deck sat the boys' nurse, and the German Fräulein who had replaced Mrs. Mayer and was to act as courier abroad.

The trip was a fiasco. Mary Perkins got very homesick; the German governess was inefficient in travel. Yet when they returned — a month earlier than planned — Henry had with him the memory of his first sight of the Alps and his first grand opera, in Paris. He had, too, one tangible treasure: a box he had bought in Dresden, about six inches square, of beautiful wood, beautifully put together. From one side of it protruded a shiny nickel handle; near the bottom was a metal pushbutton. When he wound the mechanism and pulled the button, out came the song of a nightingale, just as he had heard it in a forest in Saxony, in all its variations, from the low, rich jug-a-jugs to the hesitant, rising and increasingly rapid little cries of ecstasy. He still had it; it was in his own room, upstairs . . .

"Edward, come here a minute, will you?" Henry whispered to his brother, drawing him out from a group of young men around the punch bowl. "Listen, I have an idea."

"Yes?"

"You know the nightingale . . . Let's put it out in the garden and fool people with it; they'll be puzzled no end."

"Is it loud enough? Will they hear it?"

"We'll have to get them to walk out somehow — but let's try it, come on!"

The brothers threaded their way through the crowd, Henry in front as he always was, striding along with a confident, purposeful air, his expression one of sharp concentration. "Henry knows exactly where he's going in life — look at him," Mrs. Warner remarked to her new neighbor, following the boy out of the room with her eyes . . .

Yet crossing the ocean less than a year ago he had very nearly left life altogether: the ship's doctor, not recognizing that he had typhoid, had almost killed him and for two weeks of delirium and hemorrhages no one thought he would survive. His mother hoped never again to be faced with a decision like the one she had had to make in

Venice. "Honestly, I think I'm all right" he kept assuring her, "lots of people get fevers here, you know." But she hadn't liked his flushed face and heavy eyes — no, even if he had spent the whole afternoon painting while she and Edward went sightseeing. When they returned to the hotel the two pictures, finished, stood propped against the mirror on top of the bureau: one of the red brick shaft of San Giorgio, the other of the dome of Santa Maria della Salute, circled with its great white scrolls. He hadn't got the little cupola quite right, he said, squinting at it, getting out his brushes again, and encouraged by this show of energy, she made up her mind that they would sail.

Oh, life was terribly precarious! And then, if you had all *his* energy, and took the chances he did, what could you expect? She shivered. Mountains were his great love now; hadn't he turned pale at his first glimpse of the Bernese Oberland? The White Mountains and the Adirondacks had satisfied him for a while; then it was the Alps — lesser ones the first time — finally (this last summer) Mont Blanc and the Matterhorn. They had even set an unofficial record for the speed of the descent, he and Edward: one hour and fifty-five minutes to the Hörnli hut. Down in Zermatt, through the telescope on the hotel terrace, she had watched the tiny figures running and leaping and swinging their way down over ledges, herself swinging between terror and pride. "Fantastisch!" said the proprietor, taking his turn at the eyepiece.

Where would he go next? Engineering was what he planned for his career, but he threw himself into so many things, with such vigor . . . he might do almost anything.

All evening Mary Perkins was paid compliments on her son's promise, his engaging ways, the charms of her new house, which she received with an ingenuous little duck of her head, a flutter of a laugh. Several times she and Henry's eyes met, their look saying: we have shared so much together, you and I, we are so close — how odd to be seeing each other like this, as though from two separate peaks.

The party lasted until two — long after the incident of someone hearing a nightingale — yes, they were *sure*, and people streaming out onto the lawn to stand still and listen and nod their heads and finally — when the truth came out — to exclaim over the skill of German craftsmen. Some of the older guests left at midnight but so many stayed on that at the party's end the long driveway running past the house to the Warners' and the Gillettes' was still lined with carriages. Fireflies danced and sparkled in the woods; the long rows of carriage lanterns between made an avenue of larger, fixed lights — warm and yellow, blotted out here and there by a figure attending to the waiting horses.

On the porch steps guests waited in groups for their carriages to be brought; the young people said goodnight and made plans, surreptitiously touched hands, exchanged looks full of promises. Little Sue Campbell, moving up beside Edward, slid her hand into his and looked up at him sideways: wouldn't he show her, please, just where he had hidden the nightingale? That was *so* clever! Edward hesitated: the Campbell carriage was next but one in line, her parents were just coming out the door, but Sue's whisper — and her hair! against his ear, the touch of her fingers inside his palm, obliterated his sense of propriety. Allowing it to happen, watching it vanish, he felt dizzy with release. He led her around the corner of the house into the dark and there, the nightingale forgotten, they pressed against one another — her arms around his neck, her mouth at his, luscious as an opened pomegranate, her fingers in his curls, rolling and stroking.

From the driveway came a confusion of sounds — shouts, neighing: they drew quickly apart and listened, out of breath, ashamed. When they got to the front steps several men were standing in a circle around a figure down on the pavement, the women huddled together in little groups. Edward held Sue, who was whimpering, back and pushed forward to look. It was Patrick, the family coachman, head in his hands, moaning, one knee drawn up, the other leg oddly lifeless, like a doll's. Two other coachmen were trying to quiet a highly agitated horse, still moving forward and back in the shafts, showering them with foam.

"What happened?" he asked them.

"Broke his traces somehow while they were waiting, reared . . . something must have startled him right bad."

"What do you suppose it was?"

"Could be most anything at night. Probably a shadow that looked like a snake . . . that's the worst."

Around the injured man the consultation reached decision: the leg must be broken; where was Dr. Porter? (Don't move, Patrick); someone get Dr. Porter . . .

"I saw him leave," said Henry. "I'll go for him."

Edward took his brother roughly by the coat. "Let me go, please! it's my fault."

Henry looked at his brother sharply and saw how he was

shaking, how white his lips were. What did he mean, "his fault"?

Slowly, Mary Perkins' daily visits to the hospital, her gifts of flowers and candies and magazines to her injured servant, healed her bruised memory of the evening, over-laying it — at his recovery — with new and dramatic importance. More slowly, in Edward, the shadow of the snake coiled and uncoiled, struck and receded — the course of the invisible conflict making his eyes hollower, his face more fine-drawn than ever. At dances girls flirted with him but quickly gave up when he didn't respond. He took up Track. The following spring, having become a champion hurdler and won three gold medals, he decided to go into the ministry.

Henry, meanwhile, went to New York and studied for a degree in electrical engineering. At the same time he pursued hobbies that were more than hobbies; learned to play the clarinet; pioneered in the new color photography that was just beginning. His mother gave him a boat — a little yawl on which he cruised with his friends. He bought himself a mare ("Merrymaid" he called her) and a high red cart in which he drove her in Central Park, himself on the raised driver's seat, whatever girl he was taking out at the time seated below him, at his side. These gifts were memorable, much planned-for events; they were not taken lightly yet they happened, one after another, along with the trips, climbs and cruises — for which there were always available friends — and they were told about afterwards at their mother's white damask dinner table or the foot of her high-backed bed. In that far-off world when one traveled anywhere without a passport and a city was still a comprehensible center of civilization, when the middle-class home was a citadel of leisure and entertainment, its work done by others, its privacy and integrity inviolate — what better goal was there for a fortunate young man than to savor life to the fullest, try everything, cultivate his own skills?

Nineteen hundred. Everyone older than an infant at the time marked the year in his memory in some deeply interior way. For Henry Perkins it was, in fact, an eventful and decisive year. His first job, drawing circuit diagrams in the City Engineer's office from seven in the morning till six in the evening, not only wore him out but convinced him that he was in the wrong field. He resigned, in ill health, and sailed for Europe with a friend for a prolonged vacation. They bicycled up the Rhine valley, where intolerable hay fever changed all Henry's plans, and the two young men set off for Iceland. Had he heard there was no pollen there? Was it unclimbed mountains that lured him? Whatever the attraction, they sailed from Copenhagen on a boat that took ten days to Reykjavik and there outfitted with guides and fourteen horses and set out for the interior.

They had every kind of adventure and Henry nearly lost his life when, climbing a mountain alone, a rock against which he was spread-eagled broke loose and clattered down into the valley just after he had surmounted it. He came home from the trip with a beard and several other souvenirs: the beautiful and intricately braided whip he used wrangling ponies; boxes and boxes of glass slides;

an oil painting of two women haying under the cold, northern sky.

Iceland retained one souvenir from him. In an interior marked by glaciers, geological curiosities like mountains of obsidian, hot springs and sulphur pools, there was a geyser that spouted punctually every three weeks. It had just performed when the two explorers got to it. In his disappointment the young scientist remembered something he'd read and asked the villagers nearby for soap. Soap? Never heard of it. He settled for lard which they did have, bought three pounds and threw it into the hole. It acted exactly like an emetic; there were rumblings and gurglings, a succession of sloshes that heaved a little higher each time and then — as he delighted in telling the story — how she blew! Oh it was bully! The handful of Icelanders who were watching looked at the laughing foreigner with awe: with his blue eyes and reddish-blond beard he might be one of them but clearly he had supernatural powers. Where *was* he from?

Yes — where? What was there about that bleak, far North scenery where there were only three trees on the whole island and little stunted ponies ran through the sparse grass with their long tails blowing? Where a village was a handful of houses with turf roofs clustered above a cold bay? What was there to attract the New Englander so deeply he not only returned the following year but began to study Danish so that he might read the great Icelandic sagas in the original? Sometimes our attractions feel like memories, quite incomprehensible to the heartbeat-prisoned mind. Was it "memory" let Henry recognize the language and mythology which were to mean so much to him for the rest of his life? For recognition, of a sort, it seemed to be.

Back in Connecticut, with his beard, his new language and his decision to teach physics, he entered Graduate School. At the end of the first year he spent the summer in Hartford, in the still new house, at "55" as it was always to be known. It was the first summer — and, until many years later, the only summer — he stayed there. And for Olga Flinch, Charles Dudley Warner's young Danish assistant, it was the first glimpse of Hartford.

2

*Olga, Ingeborg, Gerda, Yvonne. Four girls is a lot, and
what an irony — that I should have only girls! Yet if the
boy had lived — I wonder . . . Maybe he wasn't strong:
why else should his twin have had such a light case
(Yvonne was hardly even red) and he go into convulsions?
That horrible, horrible afternoon: the boy dying, and his
mother hysterical, and the little twin sister — in another
house — not knowing a thing about her brother, yet they
told us afterwards how she crept under a table and cried
all afternoon and evening and wouldn't come out for anything or anybody. At three! They do say, of course, that
twins have some extraordinary communication . . .*

*If only Frederikke and I . . . but there is no communi-
cation between us any more. What can I do? She doesn't
like what makes a man a man. Yet life has to be lived —
that's what we're here for, isn't it? so I love where I can —
women who want to be loved. If we separated, Frederikke
and I, what happens to the little girls, four of them? What*

*a ghastly mistake! No, no, don't say that: you know you
wouldn't give up a single one. Yvonne, the baby, still lost,
half her life ripped away; and Gerda, so beautiful — oh
God how beautiful you made her; and Ingeborg — with
that kitten-face and kitten-sneeze and that wit — where
does a child get wit from, for heaven's sake? Such a sophis-
ticated quality! And Olga. Oh Olga: you are my child!
You are the one who sees life with my eyes (already!), who
was born with languages on your tongue, whose mind is
my mind! Looking and looking at me with those serious
eyes as I read Genesis aloud to you that day (were you
four? five?) and interrupting: "But Far, Far — how could
He say 'Let there be light' before He even made the sun
and the moon?" Yes, Olga, how indeed!*

The face of Alfred Flinch, walking alone through the
park at Kongens Nytorv, broke into smiles. He stopped,
still smiling, to poke at some fallen leaves with his cane,
turning and twisting them against the ground — this way,
that way. "Ah ja," he summarized, "life is so sad, but
then . . ." With a sigh he moved on. He was in no hurry
to go inside the Royal Theatre — he was still early for
rehearsal and the day was one of those last autumn days
before winter takes over completely when one makes the
most of what is left. Precious little it was: a few chilled
chrysanthemums in their round beds, a few last leaves,
limp and transparent with cold, hanging from the trimmed
beeches. It was the light which was so lovely — as though
the sky lined a thin shell. And the ships bawling to each

other in the harbor like homing herds, and on the grass around him, gulls.

He sat down on a bench, still thinking of Olga. A queer girl, in ways; almost clairvoyant. I don't like that — it will make her unhappy. That maid we had, Else — and the way Olga treated her, like a snake in the house: flattening herself against the wall in the passageway so that Else wouldn't brush her as she passed by. Think of it! I'm sorry I lost my temper with her at breakfast that morning, but really, I couldn't have a child of mine look at anyone that way Olga was looking at her. What a scene! The maid dropping Frederikke's plate with a gasp and running from the room, propelled by Olga's look. And my rage and yanking the child into my study where *she* never raised *her* voice — just said with dreadful earnestness: But she's stolen my new umbrella. I guess she had, too; wasn't it the same afternoon we found out she had been in prison for three years? Still it isn't good — a child knowing so much . . .

Olga knew more than her father suspected. She had begun "knowing" before she could even understand what it was she knew. Inherited memory, or precognition: how do we know things? There was the winter day when, with her parents at tea, she sat playing with her doll on the floor. A deathly quiet afternoon, with a few flakes of snow beginning to fall. The chimes of Helligåndskirken fell into their delicate, headlong cascade — like a tree shaken after a shower — then slowly struck four. All over the city, from clocks and spires, bells rang the hour or played their tunes. Alfred Flinch, face pale, body stiff from sitting,

stood up, went out in the hall and put on his coat and
scarf, shut the door behind him. He had said little to
Frederikke; he hadn't kissed Olga goodbye. For a few
moments nothing happened; the cannel-coal fire hissed and
blew, then — jumping to her feet, almost knocking over
the teatable — "Pauline! Pauline!" the child's mother
called out, yanking at the bell pull as well. Skirts gathered
around her, she ran to the window and looked out where
Alfred walked, in the direction of Kongenshaven, Kongens
Nytorv, the hotel where the members of the Royal Vien-
nese Riding Academy were staying — where *she* was staying. (Tonight she would ride the white Lippizaner horse
in her dark red habit, her plumed hat dipping to the
horse's movements, smiling her far-off smile.)

"Yes, madam?"

"Pauline, you are to follow him."

"Which way?"

"Gothersgade. Kongens Nytorv."

"Right away," and Pauline withdrew.

Bang, bang, *bang!* went the doll's head against the floor
and the child's face above it grew very pale. Her mother
laughed awkwardly: what was it, then? she asked Olga.
No answer. Only the long look between mother and
daughter as each weighed and balanced the other. At the
window, a question: why does the child look at me like
that? How much does she know? On the floor, a convic-
tion: Far did something wrong, but what *you're* doing is
worse — much worse.

The parents separated; tried marriage again for a while;
were divorced. The four little girls went to different rela-

tives and friends — Olga to her mother's brother, a minister with a country parsonage in western Zealand. But before the final sorting out took place there had been two years in Paris which were to be among the richest of her life.

Alfred Flinch, historian, newspaper correspondent, philologist — fluent in eleven languages and with a knowledge of seven more, decided to devote this period (when he was not covering the World Exposition) to the education of his favorite, promising daughter. He did it by taking walks with her, all over the city. Day after day, month after month, they walked together — he giving her the background of what they saw — until architecture and art, famous figures of history and literature slowly took their places in her mind. If he was hard and critical and intolerant of any inaccuracy this did not trouble her: his love for her and the wealth of his knowledge swept her along, past any such obstacles.

In the fights between her parents, when Olga was often called upon for discussion and mediation — she sided most often with him. An odd relationship: the child full of respect, even awe, for her father's intellect; galled and disenchanted by his pitiful inadequacies. For Alfred was a visionary, living unrealistically on the flimsiest dreams. Everything was always about to be perfect, though in the meanwhile his family fell apart; he failed in his real dream of being an actor, he lost most of his patrimony through rash speculating. And Frederikke? So lovely and magnetic she couldn't enter a drawing room without all heads turning, all talk stopping, she was still a spoiled child — unable to face problems; escaping into hysteria. More and more Olga disdained her own mother.

Living with her uncle and aunt in the country parsonage at Aarby, Olga had her real childhood. She was between ages: her cousins were much younger; the intense, dark-eyed young girl from the neighboring manor was several years older. But ages didn't matter to Olga and it was a fine place for children. The whitewashed brick church with its stepped-back façade stood by itself, close to the road. Farther back, in the fields, stood the farm whose connected buildings made four sides of a big, cobbled yard. Here it was never dull; there were always creatures to watch. Ducks and geese squabbled and preened and drank from a tub set under the farmyard pump, waddling — every afternoon at the same hour — out through the wide arched doorway and down to the village pond to bathe. Swallows skimmed over the thatched roofs and under the low eaves; in the spring there were baby pigs. Each spring, too, the storks returned to their huge nest set in a wagon wheel on the wooden ridge holding down the thatch, and each autumn, when it was time for the storks to turn south, she and her cousins and her friend Maria walked through the wheat stubble to a hedgerow where they could watch, unseen, the birds' curious preparations for flight. From miles around the assembled storks lined up in chattering rows, lifting and replacing their long red legs, picking at wings and breasts with long scissorlike bills. A leader circulated pompously among them and every once in so often, coming upon a weakling, ran it through with his bill.

One spring there was a great event on the parsonage farm. The farmer, doing his spring plowing, turned up a skull, and nearby, an oddlooking weapon. He brought them to Fru Boje who fetched her husband, and very quickly things began to happen. Archeologists arrived from Copenhagen and all that spring the Boje children and Olga and Maria spent their afternoons on the edge of the dig, watching the exhumation of a kaempehøj, or Warrior's Mound. In one chamber lay the warrior himself with his horse and dog and weapons; in an adjoining one were his personal and domestic effects. Everything went to the National Museum, where it is still to be seen.

Yet even in the warmth and stability of their new homes Olga and Ingeborg — living nearby — felt cold drafts of uncertainty and fear; today was all right, but what might happen tomorrow? They clung together, doubting people's kindness almost as much as threats of the unknown.

Meanwhile, when Olga was ten, Alfred Flinch — bitter and discouraged — emigrated to America where he found his work at the New York Public Library. And at eighteen, Olga — increasingly estranged from her mother and homesick for her father, as well as being stirred with curiosity about the New World — determined to join him. She had to stand up to the entire family's disapproval, even that of her beloved Tante Maria and Onkel Andreas. Go to America? Only criminals go to America, Olga. To New York? A young woman alone? And support yourself? Ladies don't do that and you know your father will never do it for you, don't you — Alfred is so impractical . . . I know, but I want to try . . . What will you do? I shall find work; I'm not stupid.

She had learned English at school; now she took extra lessons, spending hours at it daily.

She found the work — in a publishing house; first as a

reader, finally as a kind of special assistant to its head. Her life was far from easy. She began by living in the same rooming house as her father, but as soon as she could do so moved into a one-room apartment of her own. Maintaining it, and herself, meant the longest kind of hours, making her own clothes, making do with this and that, always making do. She managed well. The high-spirited girl whose life so far had been painful and difficult now saw it undergo an almost miraculous transformation.

She discovered she could support herself. More than that: she had abilities of which she had been totally unaware. With a penetrating mind and, for a woman of that time, an unhesitating, independent approach, she gave her employer, Mr. Harper, criticism that surprised and delighted him. More than once he expressed his amazement that English had not always been her language. But this wasn't a matter of language, she expostulated one day over a piece of writing they were discussing. He smiled slowly, looking at her over the tops of his glasses: It wasn't? No: it was thinking; if a writer couldn't think straighter than this one did, how — ever — would his writing hang together? Mr. Harper laughed. "I've told you, Miss *Flinch* (he bit off the final "k" sound crisply with a rising inflection) I've told you that you were well named." She started: what did he know about her name? He let her off the hook; a Danish acquaintance, he said, had explained to him that *flink* meant "clever."

For the first time in her memory she was free of family miseries, and her father, more contented than usual, had become a delightful companion. Meeting him in the literary milieu where they both belonged, she saw the deeply cultivated and fascinating man who, in Paris, had opened her mind to the world — but saw him now on an equal footing. They had many of the same friends and shared the day's book talk; without the sense of guilt and responsibility she had heretofore had in connection with him, it became a kind of self-indulgence to fit into her days the small attentions she was able to give him: shopping for a new coat or seeing that his room was well kept, his linen in order. Sometimes, after a dinner they had both attended, he escorted her home, seeing her into her flat with a leisurely gallantry quite different from the manners of most of the men she met.

Professionally, and through him, she came to know many people, and began to receive, as well, purely social invitations. Being entertained by the city's fine old families had its drawbacks. The young women — just out of finishing schools and very busy with dressmakers, parties and each other, were either elaborately condescending toward her or envious and silent. Their mothers and grandmothers had, first, to make up their minds whether this young foreigner who worked for her living (and whose parents, they heard, were actually divorced) was, in spite of all this, well-bred: a lady. Having decided that she was, they gave her a kind of wounded consideration — even tribute — their inclined heads and thoughtful eyes saying quite clearly to the observant Olga if more subtly, and painfully, to their own daughters: You are much more vivid, more free than we are; I was like you, once — and could have stayed that way, if they'd let me. Of course it's

all right if you are on your own, as you are . . . it would
never do for *my* girls.

The husbands and sons were openly enchanted. If Olga
Flinch was quick and clever, she was also extremely femi-
nine; she might have the ease and naturalness which came
from working with men and living "in the world," but she
seemed even more gentle and responsive than their own
women. She had, too, a look, and a style, quite her own.
When other women were puffing their hair out into larger
and larger pompadours, she went right on wearing hers like
a crown, straight on top of her head. When sleeves grew
huge and ornate, she kept hers simple and to the size that
became her medium height and slight figure. Instead of
beading and frills she wore Danish lace or embroidery and
a piece of native jewelry — often a butterfly of luminous
red enamel which emphasized the whiteness of her skin,
the naturally deep coloring of her mouth. It was a very
mobile mouth — her father's insistence on precise articula-
tion and her own fondness for words making her use it
lovingly and expressively. In repose it had that softness
which can make a woman's face look so vulnerable and she
had a way of lifting her chin, almost offering the mouth,
that contradicted amusingly the definiteness with which, a
moment later, she expressed an opinion.

But she kept men at a distance. The example of what
marriage could be was still painfully close and the man by
whom she measured all others was so superior to them in
many ways and, in others, so pitifully inferior, there
seemed no way for her to estimate them at all. Worse still,
the interesting and mature men were all married or much

older, while in the company of the younger ones she found herself strangling yawns long before it was polite to leave.

One of the most stimulating men she met was the Connecticut newspaper editor and wit, Charles Dudley Warner; his books were in every house she went to and he was now engaged in compiling a seventy-volume Encyclopedia of the World's Best Literature. He was exactly Olga and Alfred Flinch's kind of person: they understood one another at once, and Warner — conversing with her — wondered if he had not found the assistant he had been looking for to do the Scandinavian volumes of his work. He made the offer: would she edit this section for him? And write the biographies of the authors? She asked time to think it over — it would mean a lot of work, and after hours, of course. A few days later she accepted.

The years flew. She had learned (she thought) what she could do and also what, in this particular frame, to expect. Long hours, however, kept her as thin and frail looking as late parties did some of her friends, her waist as small as corsets made theirs. She didn't realize she was becoming restless; fantasies of marriage did not preoccupy her.

One day, in a large group of people, she was introduced to a Mr. Frohman — *the* Mr. Frohman someone whispered in her ear. She had already taken note of him: how could she help it? He had a face like a Renaissance portrait, and all the time he was standing talking with Mr. Harper he had been observing her, politely, but frequently and critically enough to set her wondering. Was something wrong? Her hair coming down? The bit of lace at her breast come unanchored? They met; he asked her if she was in the theatre; then, did she want to be? Yes — no — she didn't think so. She was astonished by her own confusion: she was behaving as she had when a boy first tried to kiss her. Afterwards she was furious with herself for not having allowed her mind to hear properly what he was saying; something about that she ought to be on the stage: she had the face for it, she looked as though she could act . . . Well, whatever it was he'd said was lost, though not the suggestion that she come and see him at his office — to read something for him: *that*, like a small bright buoy, bobbed about on the surface of the waves.

It was hard to keep any anchor on herself in the year that followed when — still continuing in her job — she went, nights, to dramatic school. Even training for the stage was such a delight as she had never known; she found the least aspect of it absorbing and was filled with the sense that now, at last, all of herself was being used: the river of feeling as well as mind ran freely and deeply; the walls containing it — and her — were being marvelously carved out and extended. It was intoxicating to be actively shaping and at the same time completely letting go.

Her debut on Broadway — in the second lead, with the great Agnes Lemoine as leading lady — was more successful than she had dared dream. Though acting was still quite stylized, artificiality had nearly reached its peak: the twentieth century was almost here. If there was one thing Olga Flinch was not, it was artificial; Duse rather than Bernhardt was her idol and the directness of her vision, her determination to act truthfully, from the center, were as refreshing as her appearance; in this as in many things

she was ahead of her time. She had had, in the play, to
shoot a man; afterwards, when the actors had all taken their
individual calls and the evening seemed over, there were
shouts from the audience for "the little murderess!" and
she had to reappear several times alone, Mrs. Lemoine giving her a shove toward the break in the curtain. After the
Broadway run, the play went out to California and back
and was over a year on the road.

The acting she continued to adore — even when she was
terrified that illness or exhaustion might dull her performance. They didn't; the best performance she ever gave followed an accident in her dressing room when a screen fell
on her head and knocked her out. But she hated the life —
the unchanging succession of hotel rooms and meals, the
early departures and late arrivals, the feeling of never
breathing anything but the dusty exhalations of tired plush
and neglected wood and coal-choked metal. Now that part
of her *was* fulfilled, she saw to her own surprise that it
might be possible to let it go. In hotel beds and Pullman
berths she allowed herself for the first time to say, con-
sciously: I want my children.

Between two plays she found time to accept an invitation of long standing and visited the Warners, in Hartford. How she liked Mrs. Warner! No nonsense about
her, no sentimentality, as there was in so many of her
generation. And the house had a quality — not just of
elegance, and coziness, but — what was it? Even without
children it felt so richly lived in that it almost animated
the dead, July air where nothing stirred and the sun, although out, was all hazed over so that nowhere was there

any real shade. She and the Warners only came alive at evening; in the daytime they sat out on the porch or under the tall trees, reading, while a woodthrush tried out his tunes in the ravine, an odd sound of distant banging emphasizing the quiet. Machine-presses, they replied to her question; over on Capitol Avenue where factories were creeping in.

Her last day with them was the hottest. She went up to her room, bathed her forehead with cologne, lay down on the bed in her chemise. There was a knock — Mrs. Warner, to say the young man from next door was downstairs and staying for tea: wouldn't she join them?

"Oh dear, it is so hot, and I have a headache. Do you mind if I don't?"

"Of course I don't mind. But I wish you'd come. He's a nice young man — I think you'd like him. He's been abroad a lot, in fact — how did I forget it? he's been to Denmark, and Iceland."

"Iceland? heavens. Well, I'll come down . . ."

From that afternoon there were few interruptions to Henry Perkins' courtship. It was rare that he met people as gay and vital as he was himself and with Olga it seemed to be she who irradiated him, she from whom he drew some essence quite unknown to him before. As often as possible he went to New York to watch her act, take her out to supper and introduce her to his friends and family. Mary Perkins, when she met Olga, was exaggeratedly polite to her, hesitant, afterwards, in what she said about her to Henry. This troubled him only briefly, he was so sure that once they became acquainted, the two women would be congenial.

It was, perhaps, the contrast to her father that first let Olga contemplate marrying him. Henry was so open, and kind, so merry! One could count on him, too: *he* would never go dashing off with ballet dancers and equestriennes — certainly not under one's nose. And with all this he had a beautiful mind; he was highly educated — almost European. Only — what was it? He seemed rather a child, somehow, and that treacle-sweet mother of his: wouldn't it be suffocating to have *her* around?

Strangely, the more she thought about it, the more homesick she became for Denmark. Brushing her hair and putting on make-up, walking along the city streets, visions of the land — her land — kept insinuating themselves: white farms set in the wheat fields woven through with poppies; Copenhagen on winter afternoons, the lamplighter going from lamppost to lamppost with his long wand, turning each lamp, at a touch, into a glowing flower. And she thought of all the American towns she had seen — so drab, so ugly; and Hartford: well, it was better, but those enormous, sad trees and open lawns, no walls, no privacy! Would she ever feel at home? Ever see Onkel Andreas and Tante Maria again? Other people married far from home: Maria had even gone to the Orient, she heard; now that would be lonely! Next birthday she would be thirty-four and she wanted so much to marry and have her own home, her own children . . .

Alfred Flinch came to the wedding, and Ingeborg, and Yvonne, who had recently followed Olga to America.

With the bridegroom's mother and brother and one friend
of the bride's, they were the company. The newlyweds
sailed for Denmark where Henry met all his bride's family. The family were delighted with Olga's gay young man,
and flattered that he addressed them in their own language. What visiting American ever bothered to learn
Danish?

They went on to Norway where, walking one day in
the far North, they came upon an odd creature, babbling in
an odd-sounding language. Olga listened intently. He
says, she repeated to her young husband, that he's lost
twenty reindeer and have we seen them.

"Twenty *reindeer?* What is he — Norwegian?"

"No, goodness no — a Lapp."

"How — how did you understand?"

"I don't know — I just *know.*"

Her father's daughter: languages in her mouth, on her
tongue, in her heart. And her father, meanwhile, in New
York, was being asked by the Library to catalogue a valuable new Chinese addition. I don't know Chinese, he told
them, but if you'll give me six months . . . It was the
last language he learned, one of his last achievements.

Alfred Flinch, in his seventieth year, was less bitter and
sad, more reconciled to life than he had ever been. Perhaps it was having grandchildren that did it — looking into
those small faces, one like Olga's, one rather like his own,
walking slowly down the streets of Hartford with his
grandson's hand in his. He's just the age Aage was when
he died, Alfred thought; how strange life is!

3

✦✱✦✱✦✱✦✱✦✱✦✱✦✱✦✱✦✱✦✱✦✱✦✱✦✱✦✱✦

THEY WAKE up very early, the children. Though the light
in the windows of the sleeping porch is growing stronger,
the two beds — moved right up against each other —
are still in deep shadow. They don't speak for a while —
just lie facing one another, the boy and the girl — each
surveying the opposite with one calm eye, reassured and a
little surprised by this familiar, uneventful reunion. After
all *those* adventures? Neither of the mounded shapes
moves, so precious is the warmth and peace that sleep has
generated, so hostile the areas of cold. How bundled up
they are! Quilts and blankets and flannelette sheets, which
the little girl loathes (they feel like dead moths); under
the mattresses more blankets still, printed by the bedsprings with patterns of rusty mesh; against their bodies,
knit pajamas that enclose them even to their feet. Last
night the jersey felt foreign, cold, but by now it has become an outer skin, a little damp here and there, as they
are, exhaling toward their nostrils when they finally do
stretch and move, their own sweetish smell.

"Did you wet?" he asks. Just when she's made sure!
"NO!"

"I dreamt Nippie died," she says, to change the subject. Nippie, their Scotch terrier, has such terrible mange
there are spots of bare, lavender skin on his belly as big as
silver dollars; it is serious, the doctor said, and Nannie
covers the spots each day with evil-smelling grease.

"He won't," says the boy flatly. He is four years older
than she; his voice is low and impressive.

The sun comes up while they review their dreams —
in detail, exhaustively, going carefully back to revise er-
rors. In the rising brilliance the two poplars beyond the
roof next door begin to twinkle, the late autumn leaves
turning on and off like hundreds of lights. They are very
tall, those trees — the tallest thing in the sleeping-porch
sky; the little girl often refers matters to them, respectfully
consulting their mysterious presences. This morning she
sends in their direction a supplication for Nippie when,
from downstairs, comes a brisk, prolonged, rhythmic rumble. Cook is shaking the grate of the kitchen stove.

The sound has a wild, galvanic effect: the mounds
quiver and buck; piston legs push off all the bedclothes.
Just as unexpectedly the two figures pull the whole pile
back over themselves again and lie down once more,
breathing hard.

"Where did we leave off?"

"Pat was going to the fair — don't you remember?"

"No he wasn't. He'd just been out in the cuckoo clock
with Yinkee Bibble."

"Silly!"

They laugh, look at each other for a signal, and break

out in unison, slowly and loudly, the girl's voice trembling with merriment:

> Said Dame Potato, "Hurry, Pat,
> And wash your face and feed the cat
> Then run to school or you'll be late:
> Just see—it's almost HALF PAST EIGHT!"

They shout the last three words so that even the cook hears them down through the floor. For another fifteen minutes, while she mixes eggs and cornmeal for muffins and turns the coffee mill, the children take turns with their serial story. Without beginning or end, slow and lithe and twisty as a snake, the creature of their imaginations is picked up by them, handled and passed along, picked up, passed on.

They breakfast with their father and Nannie; their mother has a tray. Nannie drinks her tea in vigorous silence, but their father eats his breakfast to equally vigorous talk. He is enormously alive, wiry, vibrant. When they first come in and he picks up his little girl to be kissed, his thick moustache and beard prickle her face and leave pink marks on her skin. When — eating — he is reminded of something (and almost anything can be a reminder) he will tell them a wonderful, appropriate story or recite a whole poem without apparently having to try at all. His quick gestures (that sometimes knock things over), his straight way of sitting or walking, flow as hard and directly from him as the pennies that shower from his pockets at the end of the day when he changes his clothes for dinner and lets the day's small change scatter loudly on the bare floor for the children to scramble after. But sometimes they lose him behind the newspaper he holds up in front of him (grasping it in the middle of the back fold, shamefully crumpling it). His attention, like a great searchlight, turns toward them and away from them, giving them their earliest experience of being banished by someone else's preoccupation.

After breakfast he leaves for the college, a mile and a half away, in the new Chalmers touring car their grandmother helped him to buy. It is a fine, big high car with brass headlights that are shined once a week, and brass gears mounted in the running board which he reaches out and down to shift. He was one of the first people on the street to drive a car; there are days when he still takes out the 1903 Oldsmobile runabout with its tiny engine and its tiller. It doesn't run well any more though, but bucks and jumps out from under the porte-cochere so that they all laugh at his departure and tease him about what they call the Cricket.

Once he has left, the house turns dull and routine; it is then that arguments break out between them and the little girl screams at having her gaiters buttoned up. If she does it herself and starts out at the wrong buttonhole, the whole thirty-six buttons have to be done over again and Nannie gets cross. If she lets Nannie do it she is impatiently pinned to a lap, pressed, hard, against a great starched bosom, breathed upon by breath from someone else's insides. Scream louder! Maybe Mother will come! All of them — even Mother, anxiously listening in her bedroom — are flung into the rapids of hurry and swim about as best they can manage. Meanwhile the nursery alarm clock ticks and ticks and the big, ornate brick house where they go to school in a room on the top floor is still a long block away.

Saying good morning to Mother takes longer today than usual though it is always a kind of island in time, not to be measured in minutes. Why is it as soon as she goes in and sees her mother she loses all her walls, her supports? Why does she melt so completely that the furies of hate, grief, fear fall all over themselves and across her prostrate self to thrust themselves loudly and vehemently on that serene bed, in that tender presence? Or — if there have been no urgent pressures — that she simply liquefies with love and rocks, speechless, in the circle of an arm?

Today there are pressures, though she doesn't remember them until she is in the room. There sits her mother in the right hand of the two brass beds, the long rope of her amber hair (exactly the color of the amber hairpins that she uses) lying over one shoulder of her pink knitted bed jacket. Without having beauty her mother is beautiful. The light inside her shines more vividly than it does in most people, animating her face so that it is always expressing something — is never dull; making her voice go up and down and move through time in an infinitely varied, improvised dance.

Her mother, seeing her in the doorway, opens both arms wide — holding them outstretched, holding the child in her bright gaze, until she has closed the space between them. For a long time they say nothing inside the hug, the child's head in the hollow of neck and shoulder, her two arms around the warm, wool-soft back. Then out of the night, composed of a dream, a picture, the memory of a rabbit lying on its side, unmoving, wearing a helmet of shimmering flies — out of all these and who knows what other darknesses — fear rises and grows into a monstrous djinn. She grips her mother tighter, buries her face deeper, so that the words that come out are barely distinguishable.

"Oh I love you so, Mummy."

"I too, darling."

They are upon her now — the violence and tears — but with this fear a strange, new dignity is born; her voice drops to a controlled whisper.

"You will have to die someday — you and Daddy," it says. A small shock strikes the air.

"We all have to die someday."

"But how will I bear it, Mummy?" She has backed off now and is looking her mother in the face.

"You will, dear, you just will." Her mother smiles and with a quick, young gesture, throws the rope of her hair back where it belongs. The djinn collapses in size; compresses itself away somewhere, out of sight.

"Now look — you must *run* — or you'll be late!"

The room is not always charged so intensely. Usually it is the place for small, unimportant occupations, gone through as gently and unhurriedly as a minuet. Often, very often, the mother — sitting sewing — tells about her childhood in Denmark, while the child plays with the sewing things, arranging and rearranging in their fragrant basket of sweet-grass the spools and darning egg, the emery that is a velveteen strawberry, the cardboard cube studded with glass-headed pins. Other times she opens her mother's jewel box and tries things on, while her mother — seated at the dressing table and following her reflection in the triple mirror — brushes and brushes her hair; divides and twists it into a long double strand (so long its ends touch the seat of the stool) and finally curls it into the crown which she pins into place on top of her head.

Best of all are the times when Mother takes out the French book and with the child in her lap points at the pictures and gives them their French names. "Canard; c'est un canard," she says slowly and clearly in her resonant voice — opening her lips as though to taste a fruit. And the child, her finger laid on the duckling in the reeds who is being fed grain by another little girl in a bonnet and pinafore — repeats it after her: "Canard, c'est un canard."

Languages; storytelling: all of her childhood moves in their twin gravity. The day begins with a story, and ends with one; at nap time she tells herself stories — under her breath, so they will think her asleep. (If anyone looks in, she is the very image of a sleeping child!)

Two years after the French, which began when she was three, Nannie is replaced by a German governess who speaks not a word of English. They go out for a walk together that first afternoon, the child feeling very competent as the guide capable of taking this stranger to Grandmother's house and back, stopping on the way to show her where she goes to school. She points to one of her poplars: "Das ist ein Baum" comes magically back to her. The street: "die Strasse"; a dog: "der Hund." At the corner, in a momentary uncertainty, Fräulein's questioning look and the sounds "Wo sollen wir hin?" are like a key turned in a lock. The child grows intoxicated with this beautiful trick of communicating — all she has to do is point, gesticulate, act, and back come the appropriate sounds, some of them so funny to her ears that she breaks out laughing. "Hübsch! Hübsch!" she shouts over and over, hopping on one foot and the other. Then, greatest intoxication of all, she makes the sounds herself and sees that this strange woman committed to her care looks at the dog, the tree, the cat — at whatever she wants her to see! They understand one another!

The house they live in, though much smaller than Grandmother's, has a lot of room for children. Besides the night nursery and porch they have a big, bright day nursery with windows looking out on the back yard. Here they have their supper, or "nursery tea" Nannie called it, seeing to it that at least once a week they had hot, buttered scones. Afterwards they rejoin their parents.

Parents, after supper, after dark, are different: turning to each other they become mystifying, bigger. When the father comes home it is morning again and they dance around him with their "Daddy, Daddy, look at me! look what I can do!" They are moons circling their sun. But once he has changed his clothes (letting the pennies drop) and talked to Mother, and then evening falls, the children drop behind and are only children again — trying to keep up, to understand, tripping over half-buried roots, getting caught in the briars of meaningless words as the parents talk.

"I spoke to Professor W. today."

"Oh," Mother looks up, startled, from her handwork, "what did he say?"

"He thinks as I do that it was a face-saving device; that we have to build back his self-respect."

"Oh *good!*"

Two pairs of eyes see with relief that she starts cross-stitching again; two minds puzzle over what was heard. They are never excluded from the family circle except for dinner parties and bedtime.

The boy is coloring a map, on the floor; Father, at his table-desk, works at a new stamp album — beautifully lettering in Gothic script or studying a stamp under his little three-legged magnifier; the girl, on a footstool beside her mother's armchair, pulls strands of wool through numbered holes in a card. If she did them right they would end by outlining a cow, but she is neither skillful at handwork nor patient: the strands get into a terrible mess on the back, she yanks at the wool and it breaks. Then the tears which had been slowly gathering, creeping down the sides of her nose, splash onto the card as she explodes into rage.

"Ich hasse das Ding! Ich hasse das Ding!" (I hate the thing, I hate the thing), she yells, jumping up and down on the hated card like the evil Rumpelstiltskin — before she is banished upstairs for such an outrageous demonstration. But mostly, when Father is not at some meeting, or going to Cavalry drill in the dull khaki uniform that smells so wonderfully, the parents read aloud. Not a children's book, or even one primarily for the children's benefit, but whatever interests them at the time. Usually it is their mother who reads; if it were not for that beautiful voice, so expressive that whatever she reads about is right *there*, in the room with them, the children would doubtless prefer their nursery. As it is they stay — their understanding trailing along far behind, falling down, sometimes utterly lost but lulled, then, by sound alone as though by the sea — pulled along by it like beachcombers, stopping occasionally to examine the shell of a single word. The shell is empty, the sea has moved out from it, but they study it, feel it, weigh it: was there ever a more fitting shape?

In the night nursery — just before the dark porch and the night's dark expeditions — the same voice (how very gentle, now) addresses her alone: "What shall I tell you about tonight?" "Tell me," she replies, "about the farm" and leans her head back against her mother's body, feeling the rise and fall of her breathing, the vibrations from her voice.

"The farm is built around a square — like this — and that is where the ducks live. Except when they go to the village pond to swim — every afternoon, at the same hour. Then they waddle out the gate, down the street, down to the water. And there they meet their friends the swans, and maybe the chimney sweep rides by on his bicycle, or the storks drop in for a drink and to wet their feathers . . ."

She clears her throat, and sings, "Stork, stork, langeben, hvor var du så laenge?" (Stork, stork, long-legs, where were you so long . . .)

The voice; the room, with its light on the wall just too high to reach without a chair; the woman with the child on her lap — I know them all. If I didn't know them and the shell of their house so well that I walk about in it at will, turning corners, touching furniture, coming suddenly upon someone on the stair — it would be hard to believe that the child was myself. I can hardly be said to "remember," in the sense of inhabiting that far-off person; only here and there are moments and incidents to which I am still vitally connected, through the senses, as by an umbilical cord. Like a series of peep shows these stand out, illuminated, clear, but whether the light on them is true or false — how can I tell? Everything else is fluid and obscure in a moving, germinating darkness. I am more related to the darkness, perhaps, than to the lighted scenes: as though it were the amniotic fluid from which I am still, continually, being born. But it is the scenes that make one's story.

4

We lived in the house; yet it seemed to me, sometimes, we belonged somewhere else. Where? Maine, where we spent our summers? The farm we went to on Sundays? No, not quite — though these holiday excursions and places took us nearer to that larger, less restricted world in which we were more at ease. They had a way, too, of softening the pain of everyday differences and conflicts, so that there was a terrible sense of loss on returning at the day's or the summer's end to one's unchanged bedroom, the washbasin with the drippy faucet, the radiator's threatening sputters. Above the rising storm of my grief I would hear Mother's "She's overtired. Get her to bed as quickly as you can." If I had fallen asleep on the way home, so much the better. Then I was gathered up without words in my father's arms and carried as gently as possible upstairs and to bed, where Mother herself (not Nannie) so skillfully undid every button and hook that she took me out all in one piece from my husk of clothes.

Nothing, then, but being held to her a moment — warm and naked — intervened between that larger world we had come from and the world of sleep.

The farm was out on the mountain, about twelve miles west of town, on the ridge dividing the Connecticut from the Farmington river valleys. The year before I was born Father had bought it for six thousand dollars: one hundred and thirty acres of land; the house in which he installed a farmer and his family; the silo and barns in which were a couple of cows and work horses. It could hardly have been a paying investment, and more than once I heard Mother call it "that absurd extravagance," particularly when she tried without success to get enough money from Father to re-cover the shabby living-room chairs. The first summer they owned it, they lived there for six weeks but found it dreadfully lonely; now we only went there as an excursion.

These outings began, in a way, with Sunday dinner. Nearly every week we shared our roast and ice cream with someone who might otherwise have been lonely — a student or unmarried professor, a visiting European, and whoever it was, that outsider made the commonplace seem less so. Everything became more vivid for being reflected in a new presence, got lifted a notch, as it were, so that we children acted up to the heightened mood. No wonder the gravy, spilled halfway to one's mouth, or the blank inability to remember the last verse of "The Jumblies" in the living room after dinner were catastrophic falls from grace! For that delighted look of confidence and pride in a parent's face if it did go right, one gladly crawled through hell.

When the grownups had had their coffee, perhaps a little glass of Danish cherry brandy, and my father, a cigar — preparations for leaving would begin, and an extraordinary variety of articles collected in the hall to be packed into the car: rugs, rubbers, sweaters and scarves, painting equipment; camera and tripod for the Lumière process photographs my father was experimenting with; reading matter for Mother, and on hot days — her iridescent silk parasol with its long handle. And always, no matter what else went along, the wicker tea hamper, packed with everything for a high tea even to a Chinese linen tea cloth to spread out on the humpy and prickly grass.

Eager to start and incredulous at the delays, my father hovered around these preparations he had caused, frequently consulting his watch, impatiently biting at a strand of his moustache — a habit which distracted my hurry-hating, slower-paced mother. Finally, with his cheerful "Well, is the North Pole Expedition ready to start?" we would be off, parents in front, my brother and I on either side of the other grownup in the back, Nippie on someone's lap. It was necessary to have this anchor in the middle, even with an arm around me, for motorcars were still like open carriages, with only a low protection at the side of the high seat, and as we careened along rough dirt roads at twenty, even thirty miles an hour, we swayed as though on the high seas. It was also extremely airy. Our car's canvas top, screwed to the windshield corners and stayed forward to the chassis by leather straps, was nearly always up — once too often we had been caught in a quick shower — but it was pleasant to keep the sides open. If it rained hard or turned suddenly cold, the sides were unstrapped and rolled down where they "buttoned" to the car's body; then we sat in a rubbery-smelling half dark, peering through squares of yellowing isinglass at the outside world.

Exciting enough in themselves, these drives had unexpected developments. "Let's go exploring," Father would say, leaving the main road for a single-lane one, turning us all into pointing and exclaiming tourists. Mostly we went looking for an old mill he had heard was picturesque and that he dearly wanted to paint. The search lasted for years, taking us down grass roads that ran out to nothing, to the edge of gravel river beds; into farmyards where we were gazed at mutely by astonished children and charged at by hissing geese. After all our efforts I cannot remember whether we ever found the mill or not: the fascination of the search was so much more important, the imaginary picture of the elusive mill grew to such proportions.

As my father drove — sitting very upright and far back, arms straight out, rather like a proud equestrian statue — the speed of the car increased little by little until my mother, who hated speed in all forms, would bring it down again with a pleading "Henry! Henry! Not so fast!" She had no idea how to drive; she suspected the whole business. Often a semi-decibel more noise from the motor rather than faster-moving air and landscape prompted her unhappy pleas. In the back seat I watched and waited anxiously for the next move: would he mind? would he slow down? Usually he did but sometimes he would protest he wasn't going too fast, and the backs of the two necks in front grew very stiff; there was dreadful silence. Humor was the catalyst — the humor that seemed to flower more easily outdoors, in an outsider's presence. If, then, in connection with Father's driving, Mother happened to relate any of her amazing repertory of terrible things that she knew "for a fact" to have happened to people, there would be general merriment again at what we called her "sunshine stories," the tension evaporated; she joined in the laughter.

Arrived at the farm in its pleasant little valley dividing the top of the long ridge into two, we stepped down from the car into scenes of every child's picture book come to life. In spring, life was everywhere around us: wiggling in fat, blind puppies; stalking, high-tailed and wild-eyed, in wild, striped kittens; running and peeping in soft new chicks. It blew and tickled, buzzed and was fragrant, in windy meadows full of daisies; licked me roughly with a calf's tongue; sucked off my rubbers with its pink Connecticut mud.

Then there was the standing around in the yard, Father talking to the farmer while his three daughters and I stood staring, or they carefully brought me chicks to hold, and handed me kittens by the scruff of the neck, their paws swimming in air, their teeth bared. I had my first unhappy taste of class consciousness, and in the house, which smelled so strongly, the farmer's wife's nasal "ain'ts" and "don't she's," as she wiped the palms of her hands up and down the sides of her dirty apron, created in me a sense of utmost desolation. It was, nevertheless, as much part of Sunday afternoons as anything else we did; it stood there, hard and unyielding as the enormous granite boulder the glacier had dumped in our blueberry pasture and which, each time, we had to climb.

I knew my parents were disappointed in the farm: children always know such things. The tangled New England wilderness just beyond the fields oppressed my mother; as we picked our way hand in hand through coarse weeds, over rocky and tussocky ground, she told me about beautiful, cultivated farms and wheat fields running clear to the horizon, the ground under them bright with poppies and cornflowers; half in fun, half not, she imitated for us the whippoorwill's compulsive calling as she had heard it lying awake on summer nights, and the loud medley of insect sounds so alien to European ears. Father's disappointment in *her* not enjoying it more was less apparent; while she spent an hour or so in the farmhouse kitchen doing her duty by the farmer's wife, he sat on a campstool in his cap and knickers in front of an easel and eagerly "daubed," as he called it, or else took us off exploring on long expeditions on foot, giving us along the way many small treasures of information about things we saw, many chances to appreciate fully some special view. "Let's stop here and take the view," he would say, making it both solemn and important.

Bodies used and stretched, and refreshed by open-air tea, minds stored with new memories — a little shadowy with misgivings about rattlesnakes and wildcats (which still abounded on the mountain) we set off for home. The valley was already in shadow; in late fall or early spring the whole drive was often in the dark. What a relief it was when we had safely reached the main road over the mountain and all danger of getting mired was over! As the cliffs of the various cut-throughs passed by, magnifying and throwing back at us the sound of our passing, I snuggled down against the larger warmth at my side and either slept or dreamed with eyes open. There was little talk in the car; there was almost no one else on the road. At the foot of the mountain, street lights began. In and out of their protective pools we moved in a regular, soothing rhythm and, to my repeated fascination, at a recurring point in the pattern of light and dark our shadow counterpart, complete in every detail — bulging headlights, strapped-down top over the collected family — passed us on the roadside grass and whizzed off ahead of us right out of sight, waiting (was it?) to catch up with us again after the next light. I waved my arm; an arm in the shadow car waved back.

Yet it was summers in Maine when we seemed to be gathered the closest and at the same time part of some indescribably larger element. The farm, after all, was self-contained and familiar, but Maine not only was approached by a sequence of important journeys, perhaps even an overnight stay at a hotel in Boston — it was another world altogether and one we could never encompass. In the sky the mountains raised their mysterious, mute heads, so unchanging yet so eloquent. On the sea — too cold to enter — the islands, tufted with spruce, ringed with their chaotic ledges, were steppingstones to a horizon one never reached — no, not even if we took picnics and went all day in a big motorboat, out so far that the waves grew higher than we were and sometimes came down on the boat's deck as though trying to trounce the life out of all of us.

There, in those first summers of my life, my parents were most nearly gods. In a community of families like our own they were the standard of beauty. "She's not as pretty as Mother," I would think, or: "that man who's almost as handsome as Father." They were, as well, the standard of age, or rather, of agelessness, in a world which contained just three categories: children; old people (anyone older than Father and Mother) and parents.

And they were omnipotent. Couldn't Mother materialize herself right out of one of my nightmares — full sized and radiant and close — to tell me I wasn't alone? Just as magically she interceded for me with maids and nurses or got a shy guest to laugh and be one of us, and on my brother's birthday she conjured up crowds of older children whom she conducted through a series of amusements as lightly as a juggler spins plates and balls.

As for Father: if he couldn't control the elements, he was in league with them. How easily and comfortably he sat across the after-thwart of our sailboat, making it go this way or that with one sneakered foot, sometimes only a finger, on the tiller! He and the wind worked together; after he had consulted it and changed the sail, it instantly obliged him by sweeping us quietly ahead of it or else heeling us far over and driving us suddenly forward into the objecting waves. If we were off somewhere on a distant island, he knew from the face of the sky when we should leave.

He and Mother loved getting up expeditions and never seemed happier than when with two or three other families we went for the whole day to Baker's, the outermost island of all. Having been left at the lighthouse keeper's dock on the landward side, we then walked across the island to the great ocean ledges on the outer shore. How expectant, yet at ease, the little group was under that enormous sky, moving along unhurriedly because of the loads to be carried, drawn with rising excitement toward the steady thunder ahead of us which, long before we got to it, seemed to thin our voices. If I tired, or couldn't keep up, I rode pickaback on Father's shoulders and so, from that height, might be the first to see our goal. Beside us, way down, Mother's skirts as she walked, swept the bleached grass and sent small earth-colored grasshoppers skipping into the air with a loud click. Sometimes, from the deep shadow under her hat, she looked up at us, shiny-eyed, her hand lightly touching Father's sleeve. Ahead of us raced Nippie, with Harry and the bigger children; other long-skirted ladies with sweaters tied around their tiny waists walked beside or behind us, each carefully protected from the glare by her enormous hat, her voluminous shirtwaist tied at the neck with a prim little bow.

The ledges were like a giant's dining hall. As though they had been cleft and fitted by Cyclops, blocks large enough to hold us and everything we had brought stood placed about at so many different levels and angles it was just a matter of the grownups choosing the best "room." Then Father and the other men would start the fire, and with Mother helping and handing him things he broiled the chops wrapped in bacon and set the coffee pot over the embers. Afterwards, backs leaning against the warm rock, legs stretched out in front of them, the grownups talked and talked — whatever about? A sudden burst of laughter would surprise us at play and make us turn our heads, or they might sing and get us to sing with them, songs that grew slowly familiar but whose words one had to pretend to know by most careful imitating of lips. How happy they all seemed! How untouched they were by any of the anxieties and heartaches which for all the day's glory clutched at my throat! Voices shrill as sea birds, snatched away by the wind, the older children moved about all over the ledges and, when they allowed it, I joined as best I could in their terrifying games. Sometimes I just stood where I was, watching the ocean explode against the rocks, following the thick white curds of foam tossed up and rising — slower and slower, in growing majesty — till they fell back on themselves into the heaving thunder below. Or Mother in her goddess-wisdom saw I had had too much and led me off by myself where I could sit for an hour beside my own tide pool observing a periwinkle's progress through a weed, making the swooning anemones shut their mouths at a touch of my giant fingers. Whether peering through that wind-ruffled glass, or playing beside the hungry sea — it was all the same: there we reached the edges of ourselves and touched the edge of a world beyond.

Sometimes Father and Mother engaged carriages and we drove to one of our own island's lovely ponds. Cars were not yet allowed there: if we went anywhere farther than we could walk, it was in an open buckboard. To its peaceful creaking we swayed slowly along past the miniature landscaped gardens of the woods on either side — so slowly there was time to study each fresh aromatic moss pillow, starred with bunchberries, each little moonscape of silvery lichen in which stood clusters of coral-red fairy goblets. Back and forth swung the fringe on the carriage top; back and forth went the tasseled end of the whip, stuck into a holder on the edge of the dashboard. The only manifest hurry was when the driver took the whip out and tickled the horse's rump, and, with a louder grinding of wheels on stones, the horse trotted instead of walked, protesting (so it seemed) by presenting us with steaming, glossy droppings and great explosions of sound.

Arrived at the teahouse with its porch overhanging the water, its souvenir counter smelling of sweet-grass and birch bark, our parents and their friends sat long over tea, eating seconds and thirds of hot muffins and jam, Father entertaining the whole group with his stories, his fun. From the little "beach" where Harry and I were catching frogs in the foamy coffee-water among the reeds, we could hear his marvelously natural, hearty laugh sounding out over the lake — as if the mountainside had been given a voice.

And sometimes he took me climbing, very slowly and patiently, till the trail ran out of woods onto the mountain's granite head, and we picked our way from cairn to cairn across bare rock, over beds of dry moss as springy as mattresses. At the top, where the wind passed over, we heard the sound of nothing, we were at the beginning of nowhere, and Father put on my sweater and buttoned it up. For a long time we would stand there, I in front of him, facing out toward the familiar landscape spread out below us, he not saying anything, holding me very close against him. What was he thinking? Was it — as he told me years later he believed — that I had been conceived here, on a Maine mountaintop? For all that he was parent and I was child, there were moments whose intimations we somehow faced as equals, places that seemed our natural, inevitable home.

5

✦❀✦❀

UNBELIEVABLE as it seemed, our parents had their own lives somewhere apart from us, in outer space. We knew where Father worked for he took us there, though to us it seemed more like play and he a kind of magician. Outside, the building looked like those we made with our German sandstone blocks: it had six pepperpot towers and wide arches over the doors and oddly shaped windows. Inside it was dreadfully dismal. It smelled as physics laboratories do, only more so for being rather old; the walls were stained a dark and shiny brown, the windows were covered by black shades through which light broke here and there in blinding sparks. With misgivings I noticed queer machines, under glass; it was like the doctor's office but dark and dusty.

But then he snapped up the shades and sun flooded the lecture hall with its steep arena of seats and he went about unrolling charts as colorful and patterned as parcheesi boards, he collected apparatus. Finally — exactly like the conjurer we had seen at the inn one summer (only this performance was just for *us!*) he showed us his "tricks." A saucer full of water under a glass bell began to boil all by itself, minutes after he started a vacuum pump nearby; clackety, clickety, the pump went on and the water as suddenly froze — its larger bubbles turned under our eyes to domes of ice. In a darkened room he let us stand in an invisible beam of "light" and we were turned into Halloween monsters with flourescent teeth and eyeballs. The more we gazed and the wider we opened our mouths in laughter the more terrifying we became. He let us pass our hands through a million-volt spark which leaped with the sound of a firecracker between two metal balls — the tiny, horizontal replica of a bolt of lightning. The air smelled as it did in the midst of a thunderstorm; the hair on our arms stood up yet we felt no more than from a fourth of July sparkler. Finally we looked into a kind of shadow box at a bewildering cross-fire of needle-fine light beams and at this he became himself intensely excited. "Look! There goes one!" he exclaimed delightedly though we could not follow or appreciate the source of his absorption. "Radioactivity" and "alpha particles" were terms not yet on the lips of school children.

The basement was very different. Here his research experiments were set up with an unbelievably complex array of wires, tubing, batteries, meters, all crossing and recrossing small spaces in what appeared as the utmost confusion, yet into this tangle he would reach for a dial to read or a screw to adjust, with the same blind familiarity with which I reached into my toy closet. Though the basement was frightening for its continuous clacking of vacuum pumps and the steady hum of dynamos, the battery room was worse for its ominous quiet in which, mysteriously, jars full of sulphuric acid were the source of power great enough to kill. On entering the basement we were given the strictest admonition to touch NOTHING, and walked with hands glued to our sides. It was scarcely necessary to tell us: we knew what had happened in the battery room; how the janitor, replenishing a battery one evening after hours, had tripped and trying to save himself, grabbed at the nearest support: a "live" bus bar. That he was not killed outright was due solely to his being attached by only one hand, and to the floor being dry. As it was, hours passed before the night watchman, noticing lights behind the foundation planting of the building, found him glued, moaning and delirious, to the three-inch band of copper. He never fully regained either the use of his right arm or his natural health.

TOUCH NOTHING! I walked, as steadily as I could, between generators like great metal snails inside their housing — their motion invisible — and the open cubes of those acid-filled jars as clear and innocent-looking as the big blocks of ice our iceman brought into the kitchen — walked dreadfully aware of every teeter, fascinated by the nearness of injury, even death. I thought of what Father had said when telling us about ice and rock-climbing and I had asked him "What if you slip?" He turned on me the full power of his level, stern look — he could look very stern — and there was a terrible silence. Then: "You don't slip," he said, the words carefully spaced and weighted with the extreme gravity of unforgivingness.

But teaching and research were not the only things he did away from home. Year after year, he undertook to serve his church, his city, the school for the deaf, a long list of charities. "*Must* you?" Mother asked in dismay at each new involvement, or sometimes with a voice full of scorn: "It's ridiculous. You don't know how to say no." Turning anxiously from the sad, firm resignation of his face to the exasperation in hers, I couldn't read the signs: was she concerned for him? Afraid he would dissipate his energies? Or was she (how I abhorred the thought!) disappointed in him somehow, the way she was with me when I was bad? In either case it meant, for her and for us, more evenings without his being home.

She, too, at this time had an "outside" life: she coached the college dramatic club. As soon as she touched this work she was transformed. Her face became more radiant; she moved quickly, with grace; all of her seemed clear, focused, calm. Much of her coaching took place right in our house, for she had each player come to her for individual instruction. She was brilliant at this and in the fury of her vision how a scene should go, a line be spoken, nothing else mattered. Shy, self-conscious college boys changed into poised young men once they had experienced her devastating mimicry of their speech and mannerisms, heard her "Now Jim, you *can't* get up in front of all those people and make such an awful ass of yourself"; everything superfluous and wasteful dropped off them; they began to *be*.

Their voices, too, grew strong and authoritative. Right

in our plain, brown living room (which had no doors, only a wide opening into the hall) she taught them how to throw their voices across distances. "Pretend it's a ball and send it, in an arc, clear to that back row," she shouted, illustrating with an "Oʜ, Aʜ, Eᴇ" that bowled into every cranny of the house and set the crystal prisms on the dining-room candlesticks to dancing. Oh horror! Hearing that great voice the first time, I thought the earth had opened and a god bellowed. Was it her anger had done it? Half fascinated, half terrified, I peeked into the room where she stood, holding the student's hand on her belly, telling him to notice exactly what her muscles were doing. Was this my darling mother? Would the young man ever come back? Then, seeing me, he smiled and after the lesson he took me on his lap and he and my mother chatted together cozily over a cup of tea and I knew everything was all right.

Scene by scene, like a plant putting out leaves, the play grew. Finding numberless reasons to go through the hall, or to stand for a few minutes behind the portieres, I learned, in pieces, the whole of the *Prince and the Pauper*; heard my mother impersonate every role in the play, heard her bc tender, eloquent, malicious by turn; heard her chastise a pupil loudly and ruthlessly or, dropping her voice almost to a whisper, say with utmost feeling, "That's right, Arch; now give it still a little more: this man, remember, has saved your life."

Harry, walking into the hall latc one afternoon, after playing football, threw down his books, his cap and mittens and was about to call out "Mother?" when he heard odd sounds from the living room: a sort of scuffle, grunts, a groan. Heart racing, he rushed in and there was his mother, half lying across a chair, eyes starting from her head, being choked to death by a man. Harry turned paper-white and gasped out "All right Mummy, I'm here!" before the two actors got disentangled. "He simply wasn't doing it convincingly," Mother told Father at dinner, "so I had to make him get rough." Father's balding head shook with laughter; Harry sat glowering, and never quite forgave her.

As production time neared, other kinds of drama took place: the hero got appendicitis; someone else came down with mumps; dress rehearsal came and the costumes had not arrived from New York. Worst of all were the love affairs that sprang up between the male actors and the town girls who took the female roles. Never, never again, Mother roared, emerging from a telephone call in which she forgot she was not roaring for a student's instruction, and as opening night approached, our house became as electric as before a thunderstorm, my mother grew into a kind of savage fury — beautiful and exciting and contained.

The performance justified all; under her direction it was of almost professional quality and for two or three evenings filled our one large, legitimate theatre. Once the imitation tapestry curtain with its sylvan scene of a rustic bridge crossing a little stream, the words "Come to the woodland across the brook" on a swirl of ribbon below it — once this had gone rapidly and magically up, out of sight, and the first scene was disclosed, the first lines spoken, the audience (one of which contained the great Mrs. Lemoine) settled down, assured, fully transported to medieval England.

Yet she gave it up. It was too demanding, too concentrated into brief periods of furious activity. And how could the real theatrical world — in which she had once been so at home, so gifted — be combined with the world she lived in now? Little by little one could feel the artist's frustrated passion for expression and perfection turn into a kind of despair, out of which she began disparaging Father's hobbies. While Father — who so loved to teach, who was so irrepressibly quick and eager — tried directing whatever she undertook, showing her how it should be done, suggesting and correcting.

"Why don't you take up painting?" he asked her one day.

"I have no talent."

"Then take up piano. Or write — why not? You used to do that."

"Oh Henry, I can't. I have to do things my own way and you want me to do them in yours."

His reply was an embarrassed little laugh, a snort of dissent. "Why Olga, I'm only trying to suggest something."

"Yes, yes, I know, but you keep interfering when I do things, telling me how they should be done. Why can't you leave me alone?"

He looked at her hurt and incredulous. I looked at each of them through a veil of misery, heart swollen with anguish. Parents were supposed to *love* one another, not peck at each other! I ached for some proof that they cared, I longed for the icy crust in which each was freezing to melt away. Over my misery the argument gathered momentum, as it so often did, their voices rose and rose until the air snapped and crackled with open conflict.

"Please," I heard myself say, and then louder, "*Please!*" They looked at me in astonishment; they had forgotten I was there.

"Please love each other!" I begged. Exchanging glances, they laughed, uncomfortably.

"What do you want us to do?" they asked, as embarrassed as I was.

"Sit in his lap," I told Mother, tears barely held back.

"Like this?" she asked, perching on his knee, putting an arm around his neck. They exchanged amused glances now; she began to play with his beard. But the giggle that came out of my not-crying was as thin as a bubble: it was as though we were all three in the photographer's studio, posing for our pictures.

For a few weeks every summer Father left us to go camping or climbing or cruising with a group of men friends. Wives seldom accompanied their husbands on such expeditions then, nor was Mother in the least athletic. Father encouraged her in the milder sports but she was physically timid and she had, as well, a handicap she concealed so skillfully that even he kept forgetting it. As a child she had broken her foot and it had been badly set; years later it was rebroken and reset, which only made it worse so that nothing but great determination and persistence enabled her to walk without a limp. I knew, sometimes, that she was suffering acutely, yet she stepped out, erect and blithe, wearing special shoes that laced like ballet slippers, and only the most observant noticed the slight twist of one foot, the hard lump on the instep all crisscrossed with ribbons.

Because of these separate orbits of their lives — particularly the times Father came home tanned and exuberant, eyes blue as sea water, to tell Mother and us of his adventures — nothing made me so happy as to have them go out somewhere together. In an ecstasy of rapture I saw my darlings go off to evening parties, my mother in her long velvet coat with its eiderdown collar, her hair carefully covered with layers of chiffon still fragrant from the sachets in her drawers, my father as sharply black and white in his starched shirt and tails as our dominoes were. Once they did go dressed up as dominoes to a fancy-dress ball, of which there were many in our town; another time Father wore a Greek soldier's uniform with pompons on his shoes and long white stockings, a starched tutu and embroidered bolero, a gold-encrusted pillbox cap. "Oh Daddy, Daddy you are beautiful!" I exclaimed. "You look just like the organ-grinder's monkey!" And he put his arm around Mother, whose eyes over her Turkish veil were all liquid light and they stepped through the doorway and out into the night.

Better still was when they went away for a vacation, or even to New York. I was so sure they were happy together then and I tried to picture them on the boardwalk at Atlantic City, of which they sent me a postcard, or here — in this very carriage driving through the pine woods at Lakewood. It didn't look very beautiful, from the picture, but it must be, it *had* to be! And they could play all day, or whatever grownups did when they were on vacation, and Mother didn't have to placate a red-faced cook, or call the plumber, or plan meals, and there would be no arguments between them, no cross looks — nothing but joy. I even found a postcard to send to *them:* the picture of two kittens playing with a little girl about my age. "This shows what a good time the whole world has," I wrote on the back.

At home, Harry and I planned presents and surprises; we learned poems to recite; we got up a play. Many times in their absence he or I tiptoed into their room to pin a drawing on Mother's pincushion, or lay a letter on a pillow, to make the sacrificial offering (so painful, so delectable!) of a chocolate rabbit, or a special candy wrapped up in gold foil. The wrapping hadn't gone back quite as neatly as it should over the nibbled place: would they notice? Would they mind?

Their return from Bermuda outweighed all others. Four years old at the time, I still lived at night in a plain varnished brown crib that was like a railinged box on legs. I had been asleep when, as though in a vision, I saw my parents just inside the door of the night nursery, Father's hand still on the switch, the room exploding with light. I sat up, blinking. How beautiful they looked! How brimming with expectancy was my mother's face, how fuzzily friendly my father's moustache and beard-framed mouth! I was picked up and held close and the crib rail rattled at the touch of the gift they had brought: a necklace of slippery little vermilion seeds, each one with a jet black eye. Nothing needed to be said: the circle was whole — Father, Mother, me. The gift was a sign. Then, at the door, about to turn out the light and leave me, Father said gravely, in a low voice: "We were late getting home because of a fog. Do you remember what fog is like?" I did, from Maine.

"We got home all right, but a beautiful big ship called the *Titanic* went down last night — way out at sea. It struck an iceberg."

And Mother (who had spent most of their vacation in bed with grippe) told, in her still hoarse voice, of their slow, blind progress up New York harbor, foghorns blowing, the bow of an outbound freighter looming suddenly tall in front of them so that the two ships had to swerve to avoid hitting one another.

I felt as though I were with them, on the deck of their own ship, the fog in my face, horror in my heart. They were here, safe, yet they were the visible messengers of some immeasurable disaster which, though I could not grasp it, hit me too. It is from that night and from no other time that I see again the spidery design of field flowers on the nursery wallpaper, how it suddenly looked sad, even sinister. Alone in the dark again, I wept.

6

FOR NINE months of the year the center of gravity in our lives was Grandmother's house, two blocks from our own. Forest Street, with its houses three or four times the size of ours, set in so much more land, could not help but impress us; Number 55, for many more reasons, was entered and visited with formality and awe — rather like going to church. Mother put on her Sunday dress and herself checked the freshly pressed clothing laid out on the bed for me: shirt and Ferris waist and long stockings; scalloped flannel underdrawers, ruffled cotton drawers; scalloped and featherstitched flannel petticoat; ruffled, starched petticoat; finally — at the end — a ruffly white dress and the wide satin sash it took so long to tie, and, under the bed, the pair of boots or high buttoned shoes, black in winter, white in summer, to be done up with a button-hook.

From the moment we walked into "55" Grandmother made of our visits a ritual and an occasion, full of the most elaborate kindnesses, the most carefully fostered sweetness. Usually right after our arrival she would lead me upstairs, "to look for a present."

"Do you really suppose there's anything there?" she would ask, taking me by the hand. "Let's go see."

She was a soft, plump, dimpled little woman with curly hair and a curly smile. The hand holding mine was cushiony in spite of all the rings with their pronged jewels. Slowly we climbed the wide stair, the long black skirts at my side rustling at every step. Oh those black dresses she wore! All stiff with tucks and bands and cording that circled them from the floor to just under her chin, and down her arms to the wrists, covering her so completely I never thought of her as having a body at all. She looked exactly like my doorstop, which was a doll dressed as a waitress whose long black dress fastened on over a weighted wine bottle.

At the top of the stairs we crossed a hall and turned into the room at the left where, between the windows and an alcoved window seat was a deep, narrow closet she called the "Magic Closet." Whenever she had been away on one of her wonderful journeys — whether around the world or only to Boston — there was sure to be a present hidden in its depths though she pretended, every time, that she didn't know this for certain.

How she enjoyed her little game, and to what extremes she played it, dextrously slipping in the doubt that heightened the joy of discovery! Perhaps, this time, there *isn't* anything, I told myself on the way upstairs, carefully lifting my feet high so as not to trip on the green carpet's

brass rods. At the closet door came the last agony of mis-
giving. "Shall we open it? Now?" she asked, both hands
curled over the knob. From her expectant look I was
pretty sure I would not be disappointed. There were
times, even, when I found the whole ritual foolish, her
play-acting offensive: what did she take me for, a baby?
I was pretty sure, but never certain; then doubt, embarrassment, all the tortures of delay vanished at the opening
of the closet and after that of the box with its Chinese
dolls' teaset, or the miniature farm from the Black Forest,
complete down to spotted cows and tiny chickens and
conical trees, their sponge foliage stiff with green paint.

When we sat down to eat, it was at a round table
covered to the floor with white damask even for a week-
day lunch. The damask made patterns of flowers or ferns
or stags at bay: if you tilted your head whole scenes vanished, others lit up; if you touched the cloth it felt as
glossy and cool as if it were wet. Silver salt cellars and
pepperpots stood in front of each plate — so shiny my face
made a wide, squashed moon in the surface of one, an
hourglass face, topped by a wen, in the other. Catching
my brother's eye I would begin to giggle, the grownups to
cluck at our rudeness. In front of Grandmother and whoever sat opposite stood two silver cows — Dutch cream
pitchers they were — tails switching over their backs where
a huge fly made the handle of a hinged cover. One of the
cows had lost its garnet eyes; both had enormous,
stupid mouths out of which, when we had berries or
soufflé, poured thick cream.

After dessert we were dismissed and went to find Nils,

the Danish gardener — a cheerful, grizzled peasant from
the island of Samsø — not at all averse to leaving his work
and giving us rides in a wheelbarrow which he lined with
a cloth to protect our clothes. Or if we were to stay till
late afternoon I was put down upstairs for a nap, with
Grandmother's old Swedish maid to keep an eye on me:
"Wee" (for Marie) who had another doorstop figure
though everything else about her was round — her face,
her head with its skinned-back hair, the bun at the back;
the thick-lensed glasses she wore as she sat rocking at the
window and darning. Against the light I could see spring-
ing from her round, pugnacious chin short white bristles
as out of a hedgehog.

Meanwhile, in the smoking room, near where the
grownups took their coffee, my father played the orches-
trelle. This was a kind of organ which could either be
played manually, or — by switching to electrical controls
— could be made to play perforated rolls like a player
piano. It had many of the stops of a real organ: treble
or bass could be brought out, notes made to quiver with
tremolos, whole phrases made to swell or recede with the
diapason. There were over a hundred rolls for it — such
popular classics as "Peer Gynt" and "L'Arlésienne," the
fire music from *Die Walküre*, Handel's "Largo." My father
adored playing these, leaning back ecstatically on the organ bench as he pulled out and pushed in stops —
shouting over a crescendo with a shake of his head and
his eyes shining: "Bully, isn't it?" I did not like it much.
I could not listen to music in long enough phrases to give
it significance and if I heard it from upstairs where it

rumbled and roared distortedly and the oboe whined out arias — it seemed all sound and fury; I pulled the pillow over my ears trying to shut out the unnamable horror and sense of doom that swirled in the air.

If I stayed with the others, I was weighted into my chair with the books Grandmother laid in my lap — huge books with illustrations by Dulac and Rackham, sometimes (blessedly!) the picture albums of French history. That pointed-nosed man with medallions around his hat, walking through an apple orchard where feet dangled from bodies out of sight: he was so much the impersonation of evil I almost loved him for it. Those battle scenes with riders being flung from dying horses! The Paris street scene at night with beggars and wretches lounging around a poet who was writing in the gutter! Whatever was happening here was real: blood flowed, people wept and I was there, among them.

What was going on around me meanwhile was curiously *un*real — even false. Everyone but Mother was playing some kind of role. Father, being so deliberately entertaining, was acting the way Harry and I did when we set out to impress our parents, and to this Grandmother nodded and chuckled admiringly as did any of the coterie of her extravagantly affected women friends who was likely to be present. When she spoke herself, it was with elaborate pleasantness. Only Mother sat quietly attentive and said little, even when she had the chance.

Sometimes Grandmother's face darkened with disapproval. "You're *not* going to the Goodwins' reception?" she inquired, turning to Mother at this bit of information.

Then recollecting her ingratiating manner, folding her hands in her rustling lap and pursing her lips, "But my dear, I think you *must*. For my sake, if not your own." She said "my dear"; it sounded more like "my hate."

Or Father might ask Mother to tell something about Denmark or about her life before she came to Hartford, much as he asked me to recite verse after Sunday dinner. A little hesitantly she would comply and then the forthright voice, stating so directly what was to be said, neither embroidering nor detracting, brought a simple dignity into the room which made us all real again. It was not for long. As soon as anyone else spoke we were back in the swamps of self-consciousness, the voices given that artificial upward inflection supposed to make them sound cheerful. What was it happened, between the heart and the word? Were the jealousy and fear and rivalry for prestige too terrible to be admitted? Was the unaffected honesty — and intellect — of this ex-actress, this girl who had supported herself "out in the world," and who was so different from all the safe Hartford families, more than her mother-in-law could bear? Duty told the older woman what to do; she affected what gentility required her to feel — and the room clouded again with the pseudo sweetness in which we either slithered or stuck.

But Mother stayed as she was; she was steadfast. Valiantly she kept trying to make some real contact, establish some relationship, throughout which her look, the tone of her voice, even her silences remained true; though controlling the distaste she must have felt, she never pretended to what she did not feel. What a strength that was! While each person in turn picked a precarious way along icy slopes, above abysses, she stood between them and us, firm on the rope.

Every five or six years the big house reverberated with anticipation: Uncle Edward was coming home, from China. There was a great bustle, though of a different kind from before holidays or other visitors. Instead of things coming out of hiding, they were put away. Wine decanters disappeared into sideboards; cards and poker chips and every game in the house was hidden; my brother and I were forbidden to play or even mention games in his presence, and there was — while he was home — not a single whist party. Poor Grandmother! What did she think when her younger son, who had her curly hair, her very laugh, who had been (we were told) so dashing and popular, became the strictest of Methodists and a missionary as well? Whatever she thought, she must have felt deepest gratitude for the conversion which came to save him — if not in time to save the whole man, then at least to heal the broken one. For broken he was — all the devils of Puritan prudery, all the howling fiends of hell-relishing forms of religion having conspired with him to destroy his manhood and very nearly to murder him outright. Then it happened: the conversion. He was walking through a friend's gate one summer evening toward sunset — a gate in a picket fence clogged with rambler roses (I knew the scene, it was described so vividly). The world, the flesh and the devil being irrevocably renounced, half of his nature eliminated, he suddenly perceived how the other half might live for both. "I have known clouds since then," he used to say, "but never again darkness."

And how proud Grandmother was of him! He had become a doctor; he had built with his own money a hospital on the banks of the Yangtze, assembled a staff of doctors and nurses, and was relieving suffering in whatever form it came to him.

He had — unlike anyone else we knew — an aura of perfect goodness. It was contagious, so that everyone else became better too. Irritability and meanness melted away like dirty snow in his presence; he seemed not to notice they existed. There was no point, I quickly discovered, in being naughty or thinking bad things when he was around for he just wouldn't recognize them. Besides, I found it easier to be the thing those gentle eyes appeared to see: it was simpler that way and it made me feel better than I knew I was.

There was great nervousness about his arrival. Would he miss the train? Had he forgotten his luggage along the way? He needed people to help him handle the world, and help him they did, gladly and eagerly, their private reactions as rushed into hiding as Grandmother's brandy. (If all else failed — as it once did when the car taking him to a speaking engagement got stuck in a snowdrift during a blizzard and the driver gave up — he prayed: out loud, unaffectedly, in entire faith. The driver was still seized by embarrassment, the prayer not yet finished when a snowplow materialized out of the whirl and came clanking to the rescue.)

Uncle Edward came home. The black cotton umbrella, the huge rubbers were taken by Wee and went into the closet under the stairs. "Why Mother, Mother . . . and look at my niece . . . dear sister Olga . . . oh my, oh my!" He looked around the family group, all the while bubbling with a warm little laugh, greeting each one of us as though we were a miracle taking place especially for him. Inside I stretched a little; something danced free for being seen and addressed.

After lunch out came the presents: mandarin coats, stiff with gold; bolts of silk like moonlight, like a tanager's breast; sets of delicate, wiry-live linen embroidered with pagodas; a Chinese doll family. He lifted them out from a battered old suitcase, all done up in paper as soft as a leaf and messily tied with silk cord the colors of parrot plumage. He brought me, too, a pair of tiny silk shoes, butterfly blue and embroidered in raspberry and green; the toes were terribly pointed, the heels a curious shape, and though too big for any of my dolls, they were far too small for me.

"They are for a Chinese woman," he said. "When a girl baby is little they start tying up her feet so they can't grow — so she will have tiny feet all her life."

I hid the shoes in a closet, miserable and ashamed.

He often told me how girl babies were treated: "Why, they don't *want* them, you know; they are considered a calamity! In a park in Hankow they had boxes nailed to the trees where babies could be deposited for disposal — like refuse. No, they've stopped that now — but they still leave them by the roadside sometimes, or on a dump. Some of the more intelligent mothers leave them on the hospital steps where we find them and take them in."

(Twice in his life he was to adopt girl foundlings and bring them up as his daughters until they had finished college.)

He told of treating patients mauled by tigers and bitten by snakes; of the thousands of refugees who appeared when the Yangtze flooded for a width of a hundred miles, and settled near the hospital in their miserable, flimsy camps, to be fed by the hospital rice kitchens. When word got around that he was a doctor he was mobbed, he said, and had to carry a pistol into camp with him — something as unthinkable as if firearms were given to Nippie.

What horrors and miseries he described to us in that dear, quiet voice that would break into the gentlest laugh over the most ghastly things! Did he ever expect people to be other than tragic, sinful, miserable? "Oh he was a real brute — getting drunk on rice wine and beating his wife — why one time she came to see me . . ." he reminisced, imperturbably smiling. Not even revolutions, or bandits firing at one another across the hospital compound, or — much later — foreign invaders who took him into custody disturbed that calm. He simply came home. Yet when he sat in one of the windows of the study, his back against the bookcase, his eye following the antics of a squirrel in the big oak, he would say wistfully — out of regions of his nature quite unknown to us: "Oh my, what joy to be *safe*! To know there are no bullets flying about, no starvation!"

And then, as soon as travel was remotely permissible after these "unpleasantnesses," he would return — often to a robbed and vandalized hospital. Exhuming his surgical instruments from where he'd buried them in the garden, assembling what he could find of his old staff, he and Georgie — the staunch Scottish wife he married and adored — would resume where they'd left off, adding as they did so, some improvement.

Both brought a gentle saintliness home with them, so that we were all a little kinder, a little better for their being there. When they left there was also a sort of relief at their departure: the sense that now once more life could go on as before.

Of all of us, Mother seemed the saddest at his going. With apparently everything to separate them — and it was almost laughable how different they were — those two *saw* one another: each recognized the other's Self. Uncle Edward never tried to convert Mother as he did the rest of us while she, on her side, concerned herself with more than his stories of China. Often, it seemed to me, she was the one who was more truly, if painfully, related to her in-laws than they were to one another.

Only she, I believe, understood Father's Cousin Mabel who — though she did not live on Forest Street — was an important member of the family. She was, poor soul, the daughter her parents got when they had lost an infant son and longed for another — the little girl dressed as a boy, trying, after her father's death, to win the approval of a superdreadnought of a mother. When a suitor at last appeared and she fell in love, she did not marry him but spun herself into a cocoon of semi-invalidism from which, till her death, she never emerged.

She lived on the second floor of another Perkins homestead — a grey-painted brick house with what my father called "an opulently double-breasted front." Here, in the southern bosom, where a curved bay window overlooked the garden, was a pleasant, softly carpeted upstairs sitting room — sunny in winter, full of plants. In the center stood a round table covered with a cloth which hung, like Grandmother's dresses, to the floor; on top were piles of books, ornately framed photographs, boxes and boxes of candy. In this room, and the bedroom across the hall, Auntie Mabel, as we called her, lived her life.

Calling on her was surrounded with more rituals and ceremonies even than Grandmother had, beginning with a long wait in the front parlor — smaller, more cluttered and more expensively furnished than any room at "55." Its greatest treasure was three Chinese crystal globes, mounted on stands of carved ebony. These globes, we were told, had been polished to geometrically perfect spheres by hand rubbing alone; the biggest had cost a thousand dollars. A fortune for something no bigger than the pink rubber balls we bounced on the pavement every spring! I was not allowed to touch them lest I smudge the surface but I almost hypnotized myself gazing into those three little worlds of solidified light whose weight and texture could only be divined; which held in focus — on the tips of ebony fingers — a whole room, including our tiny, inverted images.

Sometimes as we waited Aunt Mary, Mabel's mother, came to greet us — a brisk and authoritative personage with whom there was no contact: she passed over the heads and beings of children to the grownups with them.

Then we would hear Auntie Mabel's voice — the softest and most honeyed I've ever heard — as she called to us from the head of the stairs.

"Will you come up now? *Dear* Henry and Olga! *Dear* children!" This last as we were in sight, on the stairs, and she leaned over the banister in a wide shower of laces and scarves and bows. She never wore anything but negligees in the frosting colors of those French christening bon-bons called *dragées* — all of them made to her odd measurements, most of them finished at the neck with lace-edged round collars which tied with wide satin. Though the house was always on the point of being exploded by its hissing radiators, she wore a scarf or two as well and — when she sat down — a knitted throw over her knees. Or what there was of her knees — for Auntie Mabel was almost shapeless. Small in stature — I think she was little over five feet tall — she must have weighed at least two hundred pounds. She felt enormous, soft, warm; she was always a little damp and after greeting us and seating herself on the bepillowed couch against the wall, would wipe her upper lip with a little ball of handkerchief kept somewhere in that mountain of chiffon and lace and wool.

We sat opposite, in rockers and Windsor chairs, while she asked us what we were doing and what had happened since the last visit, our parents — especially my father — putting in explanatory bits and urging us on if shyness restrained us from telling about some triumph at school. All these trivial, halting accounts she followed with deepest interest, a little out of breath (which she always was), laughing with appreciation, putting in from time to time, "Oh Evelyn dear, oh darling Harry." I cannot remember her ever telling anything herself — what was there to tell? Nor can I remember any particular comments she made or any response transfused with her own thoughts. Everything we said came back to us reflected warmly, uncritically — more unblemished than, in reality, it ever was. Even my father glossed over what I knew had been an unpleasantness; events tended to be polished and shined in the telling. All the while she held us in turn in the gaze of her marvelously beautiful, dark brown eyes — stroking with quick, fluttery gestures as she sat there any of the numerous cats who slid in and out of the room, hid under the draped table and sat curled up at her side. When everything had been told, the poem recited (sometimes the piano, downstairs, played) she would get up and offer us candy from the boxes on the table and walking heavily to the south window show us a new plant or a flower beginning to open. It was the signal for leaving: for the enveloping hug and damp kiss, the last loving *"dear* little child." A trifle embarrassed by our everyday selves we withdrew from her presence — the priestess of unquestioning sweetness — and walked downstairs again, to be called to and waved away a last time from the figure at the top. Out on the stoop, adjusting his hat, my father, suddenly speaking now in his everyday voice said, "You always give her a lot of pleasure, you know."

Just once I saw her out of her rooms: on my seventh birthday I was told she was coming to bring me something. Auntie Mabel, coming to *me?* That mysterious, benign, not-quite-human presence — the priestess torn loose from her temple? It was unimaginable, yet she came, and I ran out into the street in front of the house where she sat high up in the back of her mother's limousine —

surely one of the first in town. Though she was not in a candy-colored negligee, the creation she wore — of a rich, dark puce — was just as loose and nightgowny. The pale, flaccid face with its large eyes was shaded by an immense hat swirled with ostrich plumes. One hand thrust through the supporting strap at her side, the great tented figure leaned far toward me as I clambered up on the running board and handed me a little jeweler's box in which lay my first watch. (I still have it. Often when other, newer watches are being cleaned — is the world that much dirtier, are watches that much more permeable? — I put Mabel's watch on my wrist: it keeps perfect time.)

These main figures were the family gods and goddesses who stood — a little larger than life — behind and above the figures of my parents. Other, more distant relatives came and went in the background and at Thanksgiving or Easter we were joined by Uncle Will Dwight — that baby brother of Grandmother's who had survived to become the hearty and robust owner of the Massachusetts newspaper he edited with his equally hearty wife. Then the round table grew into a huge ellipse — at one end of it Uncle Will with his red cheeks and tremendous laugh, elsewhere his son and daughters who, though my father's first cousins, were nearer us in age, all of them with voices made loud from shouting at their deaf mother. For the few hours they were with us the house rang with political discussion, bursts of laughter, excited tales; the only time the hubbub subsided was when Aunt Minnie leaned forward and in that softly damped, suspended voice of the deaf, spoke with quiet and compelling dignity of one of

her many community activities. After they had gone we
hung like leaves after strong wind — my mother at once
elated and bewildered by so much zealous pioneering and
overflow of energy, the vibrations of so many Connecticut
voices.

They were the most real of Father's relatives. What was
it which so separated the others from us? Grownups must
always be a mystery to children: what lives can they possibly have, sitting there talking and talking, shedding a
shower of kindness and smiles? But our communication
was so hazy and veiled that few things it seems to me
ever came through — direct from one being to another —
and even the one real contact with my grandmother, during
her final illness, was half hidden. She lay propped up on a
stiff horsehair couch across the room from her bed — her
curls piled up as prettily as ever — when a nurse crackled
into the room.

"Be a good little girl now and look away," said the
voice from the couch — addressing me in an undressed
tone I recognized at once as different. I saw the hypoder-
mic syringe in the nurse's hand, and my grandmother push
away the blanket before I got to the window and looked
out — blind with self-consciousness and curiosity — at the
motionless winter trees. I knew, vaguely, what was going
on: I resented, bitterly, being turned away. Then I heard
the blankets rearranged, the nurse withdraw.

At the end, when she was dying, it was my mother she
wanted at her side. The daughter-in-law so unlike what
she would have chosen, the foreigner whom her conserva-
tive community could not quite accept or understand,

was more real than anyone else; Olga stood closer, it seemed, to all that now mattered.

Our relatives were the bestowers of gifts — something which automatically made them into minor deities. Gifts were their expression, it was a bountiful era, and they could afford to give. Many children still died of diseases, then; let us give them things, said our elders, let us make them happy for we may lose them any day. Each of them in his or her way — Grandmother, Auntie Mabel, yes — even Uncle Edward, with his marvelously close and paternal God — had the same message for us children. "Life is a Magic Closet," they said, "shall we go and see what is in it for you?" But Mother said, "Life is strange and terrifyingly real." "And wonderful fun," said Father.

7

AFTER Grandmother died, everything changed. It was mysterious: here we all were, Father, Mother, my brother and me — we looked the same, yet inside us, and between us, the weights shifted and strange new designs appeared. It was what happened when I turned the wheel of Grandmother's kaleidoscope, and with a long rumble and lots of small clashes the same bits of glass reassembled into entirely different forms. I had a fever when they first gave me the kaleidoscope to play with, so I tried to attribute the uneasiness it gave me to being ill; I knew there was some other reason. "You never get the same design twice," said Father. "*Never?*" I asked. "No. It's just a series of infinite probabilities." (There it was again, that terrifying word: infinite.) Snow crystals were never twice the same, either, he said, but each one of those, I thought, is created new — its own small star falling freshly out of space. These bits of crudely colored glass I came to recognize — the ruby one with a chip, the four bottle-green triangles —

they didn't change; one turned the wheel and willy-nilly they tumbled about till they settled momentarily into other configurations.

Father was made acting president of the college. He had always done many things outside home, but now he belonged less to us and more than ever to the world. When he came home for lunch, he was full of problems; he and Mother had long talks about them behind closed doors; sometimes he wore a preoccupied look, which he had never done before.

And he took a kind of Giant's Step away from us inside himself — into some other dimension and nearer Grand-mother. On Memorial Day he took me out to the cemetery with him and we laid flowers on her grave. I felt honored and happy he should want me beside him and babbled all the way, but talkative child as I was, something in him kept me still as he stood at the grave, hat in hand, staring down at the mound under its corsage of peonies. Seeing his face I was ashamed of feeling nothing at all. Suddenly he moved, oddly and jerkily, and I heard a tight, strained voice that wasn't his at all.

"That isn't Mother lying there," the voice said, and roughly (for him) he led me away.

That wasn't Father, either, at least not the one I knew.

Mother, too, moved further from me. With all the entertaining now required of her, I lost her to caterers and telephone calls, faculty wives and droves of students at the same time that the German governess she engaged for me almost usurped her place. Like all our Fräuleins she was infatuated with Father and critical of Mother so that we were very stiff together — she and Mother and I — while with Father, whom she resembled in her zest and versatility, there was a holiday mood. At breakfast he would reminisce happily, in German, about his travels, his own German governess; he quoted poetry; he recited — with what joy! — whole stanzas of Schiller's "Der Taucher." "Just listen to this," he said, about the water at the foot of the cliffs: " 'Und es wallet und siedet und brauset und zischt/ Wie wenn Wasser mit Feuer sich mengt' — doesn't that sound exactly like what water *does?*"

With all this, my brother, too, leaped overnight into a new status — that of young man of the house. How intolerably superior he became! He seldom condescended to play with me any more; "You wouldn't understand" was his stock reply to my questions. Goaded beyond endurance one day, I retaliated with the threat that I was going to kick him, "Right *there!*" I yelled, indicating the ever fascinating, ever mysterious crotch. "Don't ever do that," he said with dreadful intensity, "to me, or to any boy, do you hear?" So boys were that special and vulnerable, were they? Those little things they had deserved more respect than what I had, did they? Well, Harry could go and play with his fine, big friends, then: he was no fun any more in *my* world. In the fall he would disappear into the unimaginable wildness of a boys' boarding school and, from seeing this happen in other families, I knew what that meant: once they reached this point boys came home less and less, they led their own lives. Suddenly the four years between us which we had once minimized to nothing stretched into almost a generation.

And wasn't I myself changing? Or, rather, changing more and more rapidly? Little by little, in a slow unfolding of incident, dream, scrap of conversation or moment of insight, my body and I had been growing apart. The little creature that charged about the nursery naked after her bath, delighting in herself, roughhousing with her naked brother — whose awareness of herself had been as smooth and seamless as the skin of her flat little chest and protruding stomach — now gradually divided, like the first spear of a hyacinth, into stem and bud. "I" was mysteriously freed to observe "myself"; "self" was left to be ashamed of its own body. Was this freedom, or its opposite? Whatever the nature of the division, its quotient was the sense of shame, the pain of guilt. Now that I went to church regularly, the glaring light of religion made these shames and guilts almost insupportable; becoming aware that my body had the mysterious, startling capacity to give me pleasure, I grew as hot with the sense of sin as must be those cowering beings in pictures of hell, whom devils were prodding with pitchforks into a fiery abyss. In this, neither parents nor governess could possibly help: they were too pure, too good, to understand. Entering the inner darkness from which there is no way out than through the opening of unashamed love, I felt horribly, irretrievably alone, and — worse still — the intimations that came in to fill this emptiness and share my solitude were monsters. I heard my governess's dark allusions to the male sex and to something that happened between couples. There was nothing definite — only quick, black suggestions appearing and darting off like bats on a sum-

mer evening, but somewhere deep inside me they roosted,
and grew. How horrible they were! What secrets grownups must have! Was it that which made their faces sometimes so sad, so anxious?

I looked at my parents with new eyes, becoming more
and more aware as well of how different they were, one
from the other. Dissensions and quarrels were familiar
but the unity I had rested in as a small child grew harder
to find and further away, like a vanishing horizon. The
little house we had left for the president's house on the
campus, and would never go back to now, assumed the
same relationship to our present lives that outings had
once assumed to it; we had left behind us somewhere that
cozy world of climbing into bed with our parents Sunday
mornings, of giving some shy young man a trip out to the
farm with us, for larger, more serious endeavors carried
out by changed and more separated selves.

Certain areas of difference grew familiar. When it came
to money I knew that Mother was sure to have trouble in
asking Father for what she needed. She was direct when
she should have been subtle, and the other way around;
she anticipated defeat so that at the first barrier she was
already heated and pressing. If the amount was unimportant in size, Father would merely say with a laugh that
we'd end in the poorhouse yet and make a joke out of it,
but when it came to large amounts, or what he was giving
to charity or in help to some dependent (of which he
seemed to have many outside the family circle) he took a
rigid, even defiant stand. "He never talks it over with
me," said Mother sadly; "he always seems to have enough

money to go camping or cruising or whatever *he* wants to do." The landscape of their economy was everywhere rough.

Their ways with people were parallels which did not deviate. Father was instantly and immensely at ease with anyone — anyone at all. When traveling, he talked to whomever he felt like talking to, and said what was on his mind, sometimes oblivious (it seemed) of the other person's state of being. When Mother tried to get him to see this, he pointed out the amazing friendships he had begun this way, and tongue-in-cheek he relished telling how at the circus side show he had gone up to the three women from Africa who were part black, part white and "as mottled as leopards." Addressing the eldest, he had asked, "Do you mind telling me how you ladies account for your unusual complexions?" "Oh Henry!" Mother laughed, making the sort of *mou* a mother does at a son's prank. "But they loved it!" he defended himself. "We talked for twenty minutes!"

Next to this extraordinary friendliness, her approach to others was reserved, even aloof. But let any real meeting take place and the relationship went deep and lasted long, absorbing some of her frustrated artist's passion for expression and perfection.

It was the same with religion; Father's faith was traditional, orthodox, and apparently as uncomplicated as my own. He never missed the eleven o'clock service at the beautiful white Congregational Church where I usually sat with him in the family pew, and the minister, impressive and stern as one of the prophets, preached to us from the high chancel. Addressing us in a resonant, often booming voice, head trembling as he emphasized a point, he was like a pious bulldog shaking sin to pieces in front of our eyes, barking warning of the flames of hell which were about to erupt any second through the ornamental hot air registers in the floor.

Mother seldom came with us; she didn't like being preached at, she said. But at Sunday dinner, knife deep in the roast, Father gave her every single week a synopsis of the sermon. One of his duties as a child had been to call on his deaf grandmother after church and tell her briefly and accurately what the Reverend had said. He did it brilliantly, nor did he ever get over the habit, no matter how cleverly Mother tried to divert the inevitable. Sooner or later, we knew her attention would be lassooed, she would have to submit, but in the meanwhile we observed, fascinated, her skill at lying low, at feigning inattention, at creating distractions.

It was impossible to put a label on *her* religion: she didn't go to church; she gave no outward signs of piety, yet her faith was deep and persuasive. She believed. She believed in the reality of the spirit and the deceptive nature of the outer world; she believed in the limitless power of love; she believed in life. As my child's image of God began to dissolve into something else, I apprehended with increasing awe the magnitude and intensity of her vision.

How queer it was! Father so predictable, outgoing, apparent; Mother all volatile, receptive, inner. Were anyone else's parents as different as that?

By the spring of that year we were in the War. There was a "preparedness parade" we watched from the parlor windows of a very old, very little lady called Mrs. Mayer, who — Father told me — had once been his teacher. For hours the parade went by us — in her room full of cut-velvet furniture, collared and cuffed with antimacassars, smelling of cats and stale cooking — hour after hour of men and boys, a few uniforms, a few bands, a great many placards. We didn't seem prepared at all.

As if in reply there was another demonstration of the very first tank, which we watched clank up to a specially built little house and crunch, crash, crush it down, going on to splinter a grove of trees behind it to matches and leave in its wake a flat pile of debris. (What would happen now to whole villages? To *people?*)

And we saw the arrival of a new type of plane — like a big kite, with lots of struts between the wings and, sticking out of the body of the plane, the helmeted heads of two men, not one. As the plane rolled to a stop in the dandelion-studded grass, a man near us in the crowd said in a loud, enthusiastic voice: "They can *shoot* from that plane! And drop bombs on cities!"

In the Berkshires that summer we grew vegetables till our arms and backs ached, and Mother canned them, standing red-faced over the stove in the terrific August heat. We knitted, too — mufflers and sweaters and pairs and pairs of coarse grey mitts for the men in the trenches next winter; and my parents followed the course of the war with increasingly grave faces, losing themselves in maps and reports from which they returned to other matters with deep sighs.

Each weekend Father drove out from town with a bundle of plans and blueprints, reporting to Mother on the progress of alterations to Grandmother's house. It was ours, now; we were to move into it in the fall. Grandmother's house! Where presents came out of closets and there were attics and cellars full of wonderful things; where there were thousands of books; where there were acres of land on which to play, even deep woods, and at the bottom of the ravine, a river!

But to them it seemed a serious and difficult affair; there were many quarrels. Father would tell Mother how he and the architect had decided a certain thing should be, and if she did not say anything, he would ask her why. Because, she replied, she thought there might be a better way. "What way," he asked her, and she told him. "But Olga, you don't understand, we can't do it that way: with the door here, there isn't room." And these conferences — the ones I heard — all ended the same way: "It is your house, Henry; do as you please."

We moved in. I was given the room at the head of the stairs — the Magic Closet room — whose presents seemed childish now in comparison with this having a room of one's own, with a fireplace and a window seat full of pillows in which to read, where the only distractions were squirrels — huge and fat from kitchen handouts, flirting their plumed tails on the roof of the kitchen porch — or the click of falling clothespins as Magda, the Swedish laundress, gathered in the washing with her round, red arms.

Beyond was a street full of children who assembled afternoons after school, first at one house, then another;

played in different gardens, climbed each other's trees, were given cookies in a succession of kitchens. The enlarged and enriched world of my own home was simultaneously multiplied into a paradise of open front doors and unfenced gardens. Heaven fell into my lap.

Evenings, I had dinner alone with my parents. It was announced at seven by three muted tones struck on a Chinese temple gong; I dressed for it in a new velvet dress with a lace collar. Then at the candlelit mahogany table — silky under one's fingers, its plum-dark surface full of cryptic designs and layered vistas — I sat between Father and Mother and they talked to me as though I were another grownup, about grown-up, far off things. At dinner, I saw, they shed the day: no matter how much he had done, how tired he might be inside, Father was always merry; he told stories, he answered my questions; and Mother — serene and queenly with her crown of hair, the trailing sleeves of her tea gown — was as charming when we were alone as when the table was circled with guests.

What, then, was the shadow upon us? Was it that fourth place, opposite me, which was always set? Every plate and piece of silver was there — exactly like our own; the maid even changed those plates when she changed ours; only the water glass stayed empty. Who was it for — that place? The table looks better that way, said Mother, instructing a new maid. To my questions she only shrugged and smiled. But sometimes I fixed my eyes on the two curlicues of the chair, and waited for a pair of shoulders to obscure them, a pair of eyes to meet mine. There was no one.

On the tall screen between us and the pantry door, the eagle went on killing the snowy egret helpless in its talons; the flock of small birds flew away from the screams of its dying — over the bamboos, out of sight.

8

As LIKELY as not, we were still at dessert when Betsy appeared, after lunch, her eyes looking about brightly for adventure, her head held as pertly and inquisitively on her thin neck as a bird's. She was the closest I came to having a sister, and though we looked so unlike — she dark and small and quick in speech and gesture — we complemented one another perfectly as children sometimes do, all unaware of the rareness of such mutuality. Her grandfather and mine had been best friends; our fathers had grown up together and we had been wheeled side by side in our prams. Now we lived only a few houses apart and she spent as much time in our house as in her own.

The house, when we were together in it, we considered as our special, private province. The things in it existed for our pleasure and we alone held the keys to their mysteries and meanings. My parents were, on the whole, obstructions to our proprietorship. Father, at work in his study, kept us from our best books and was the cause of our having to keep quiet, while Mother, who might be anywhere from attic to cellar (and often appeared to be everywhere at once) stopped being my mother and became our common foe. Poor soul, how Betsy baffled her! She looked at her as though at a strange bird in the nest — a mercurial, part-time foster child she could not treat as her own and who converted me — her own daughter — into a changeling. For as soon as Betsy appeared my color heightened, I talked faster, I was very brave and fresh. Even the tempo of the house quickened as furniture was moved about and banisters shook and closets strewed their contents all over the floor. Or else — most disquieting of all — we dropped out of sight and hearing as completely as if we had gone out, yet no one had heard the front door open and close and we had positively not been seen.

If Mother was disquieted by us, we were as puzzled by her. Sometimes we discussed our parents, gravely trying to figure them out. There were strange, even repulsive things about them we didn't understand: my mother has *hair* there — I saw it once — does yours too? What do you suppose they were doing? They *wouldn't* let me in, and you know what I heard? After such talk, my parents seemed utter strangers to me. What odd creatures they were, after all, and how curiously they spent their time — Father, when he was home, at his desk for hours on end, never even looking up if we passed the open door with suppressed giggles, Mother so seriously absorbed with the dullest objects: piles of linen, packages, woolens she seemed forever either to be taking out or putting away.

Upstairs, downstairs, in and out of rooms she went, carrying, putting down, examining, sorting — limping a little as the afternoon waned, her hands getting dingy, her skin dry.

We, on the other hand, when we were not playing, led creative lives: we were writers. Often we were already planning what we would write on the way home from school, so that we walked more and more slowly, swinging our schoolbags by the strap, thoughtfully nudging along with one foot a lozenge of grey ice, or — in the spring that came so desperately slowly and disappeared so fast — the little gummy bouquets of fallen maple flowers. Beside us, water hurried along the gutter and rushed with a final "cloop" into the echoing drain; we interrupted ourselves to drop in sticks and watch them whirl over the lip of the falls or, if they got caught, do a terrible, convulsive dance before they subsided in imprisonment and defeat, their bark shredded, the pale pith exposed.

Each day we studied the weather for signs. If it was fine we would spend the afternoon outdoors, with the gang, but on all those in-between days we wanted it to be bad enough for staying in. Hopefully we prophesied it would grow worse; we swallowed hard to see if our throats weren't just a very little bit sore. Minds made up, we walked as fast as we could without once running or stepping on a crack — two stiff-legged, wind-up figures growing hot and flushed inside our serge bloomers, our floppy coat sweaters.

We wrote in a corner of my brother's room, behind the upright piano. The triangular space where this stood across a corner, we furnished with pillows, a gooseneck lamp and a cooky tin and named "the I" — short for

"Inglenook," a word we didn't quite understand but which had exactly the right combination to our ears of snugness and importance. Having climbed over the top of the piano and dropped down the other side, we spent whole afternoons composing, in perfect harmony, zigzagging at random between stories and poems, getting out what we wanted with the directness of bees. Neither distracted the other; we worked better for proximity, for being able to whisper from time to time, "Listen: listen to this . . ." If footsteps neared the room, out went the telltale light; if they came in, we sat — pencil in air — nothing moving but our eyes, till the steps retreated and left: two rabbits in a patch of clover.

Climbing out tired and cramped, we tried to sense what was most important to do next, waiting for the house with its store of treasures to speak to us. There were certain objects it was necessary to examine several times a week: the tiny Chinese sampan all in silver, even to the sail, and the rickshaw whose wheels really turned; the "walking leaf" beetle from India, pinned into a glass-topped box, so perfectly camouflaged its legs were like smaller leaves caterpillars had eaten; and in my room a miniature dog sled made by Eskimos which Father had brought me from Labrador and whose odd smell was so captivating we inhaled it till the room went black and disappeared.

Occasionally, as a treat, Mother took us with her to the third floor with its many locked closets. In the semidarkness outside the closed doors of the maids' rooms Great-grandmother's music box stood on its own five-foot table of exotic woods. We were not allowed to wind it ourselves, but once wound up for us it played for twenty-five enchanted minutes. While Mother was busy with whatever she was doing we watched, hypnotized, its great brass roller bristled with pins majestically plucking and releasing, with exquisite precision, the teeth of a long metal comb while — at the back of the box — five silver doves waited with outspread wings for the exact moment to strike with their beaks five silver bells.

If Mother had to go to the attic as well, we blissfully followed her through the ritual of taking the key off its hidden hook, unlocking the door, and searching in the dark for the portable light on its yards of cord. Unwinding behind us as we walked, the cord thrashed and buckled like a hideous snake as we neared the closet at the far end. Another door to be unlocked — and there, on a hook, demurely covered in printed calico, hung the real skeleton Uncle Edward had had in medical school, its legs doubled up to save space, the skull leaning at a contemplative angle. Opening and closing the hinged jaws, bending the clicking fingers which went on swinging a little after letting them drop, we shivered with ecstatic horror.

We let the cellar frighten us, too, as we wandered about in its gritty dark and set the box traps in which we hoped to catch mice alive. Footsteps sounded ever so faintly overhead; right beside us something knocked on the pipes and the boiler hissed and gulped. Then making us gasp and clutch one another, Nils would appear. "Ja," he said, putting his head on one side and shaking it, "it's a funny thing, now I *know* there's a mouse in that wood." Giving us elaborate theories on the ways of mice and the art of trapping them, his round head and waving arms made giant gestures against the deep spaces behind him; you would have thought he had nothing on his mind but gratifying our whim. "Ja, I'll get him for you girls yet," he wound up, and jammed his evil-smelling pipe back in his teeth at a forty-five degree angle to his grizzled chin.

Father seldom had time for the two of us, but when he did he put his arm and his affection around Betsy as easily as me. He was glad that with my brother away I had this almost sister; he found her entertaining; "That amusing 'fratz,' " he said about her face, but not until I was old enough not to mistake his meaning.

We loved best to have him tell us ghost stories. How gloriously he did it, relishing and dramatizing every horror to the utmost yet with such a merry look, such a thin membrane between terror and amusement that we were never *really* frightened. Or were we? Under the enchantment was a delicate warning rattle — like that of the skeleton upstairs; one could never be quite sure . . .

Once, when we hadn't heard Mark Twain's "Man with the Golden Arm" for a very long time, we persuaded him to tell it to us even though the sun was still out and we had to pull down all the shades in the room to help make it dark. We sat on the fire bench, the three of us, facing away from the chinks of light, he in the middle with one of us in each arm. The arm was important: at the delicious and terrible climax, after the murdered wife's ghost has whistled nearer and nearer in the windy night with her querulous "W-w-hh-h-e-e-ere is my golden arm?" and pounces on her victim with that hideous "You've got it!"

he grabbed us, hard. Mother disapproved of it. "They won't sleep tonight," she said. Was she a touch envious? She shooed us outdoors to play, telling us we hadn't had enough air.

Reluctantly we went, to spy on the gang, but before we even heard their voices we slowed down, disoriented, our own harmony first jangled, then silenced. Was it loneliness we felt? The abrupt sense of separateness artists and lovers suffer on returning to the crowd? "Don't let's spy on them today," we said; "maybe they'll let *us* play, too." Joining them was like exchanging a ferny hollow in deep woods for the blazing, windy roar of an ocean beach — shrill with gulls and blowing sand, the nervous dance of waves.

The crowd circulated from house to house in a roving, inquisitive band — avid for experience, fantastically sensitive to every variation of weather as to the fluctuating moods of mothers, cooks, baby brothers and sisters. They were locusts; they were caterpillars munching on every leaf; they were prickly as sea urchins and sensitive as sea anemones. With each other they were inquisitors, lovers, Machiavellis, Boswells, Hannibals and Rolands — one moment with an arm around a friend, the next leaving him abandoned; spying today on his secret clubhouse, tomorrow entering with him into a blood-pact, a secret alliance against everyone else.

Outwardly they varied as though members of different species — heights disproportionate to age, one dark-skinned and another freckled; one all compressed energy, another attenuated and vague. Yet each was hawkeyed about the other's dress and appearance and as ready to rush and pick at a conspicuous one as underfed poultry. "Yah, yah, Ellie's got her arctics on!" and "Tibbie Day, what's that — a stye?" When neck cords were taut from shouting, spittle gathered at the corners of mouths and voices were shrill, was there anything to distinguish them from street urchins except the houses at their backs? The dignity conferred on the whole street by its majestic trees? Only indoors. There the children read hungrily: there was little else to do when alone and there was so much time in which to do it. And together they played word games and formed literary societies. Spores of the Nook Farm tradition and its unusual inhabitants seemed somehow to flourish on the street like toadstools after rain. They sifted through everything.

We joined the crowd. Not only did the bond between Betsy and me snap with an almost audible twang but our eyes, unexpectedly meeting the other's, flared with challenge. We defied one another; oh, *her*, we each thought.

Little girls are chameleons. "I can tell by your voice whom you've been playing with," Mother used to say. If changing to the earth color of solitude was instantaneous, turning the vivid colors of the crowd was slow, made difficult by one's strong sense of being different, one's acute discomfort at having to wear — like unbecoming hand-me-downs — this compulsory garb. I was bigger, blonder, paler than anyone else and I still had a governess; my mother hadn't gone to Farmington, she was a foreigner . . .

But in the evening when we each returned to our own homes, when I pushed shut the heavy oak door and breathed the familiar, comforting greeting of the house's smell (what was it from?) then I became another person still — stripping off, along with outdoor clothing, the weight and constrictions of competing, challenging, defending. It was as wonderful to do this as it was, in winter, to be rid of the soggy woolens to which little balls of ice fastened themselves like burrs, to take off the ugly black overshoes to whose soles pads of dirty snow became firmly hammered.

Sitting at the foot of the stairs where they swept out into widening curves, I shed it all, while over the stair landing, and duplicated in each of the tall windows, the Japanese bronze temple lamp shone like an autumn moon just clear of the horizon. In that soft half-light all was stillness and peace — such stillness my mother usually heard me even in her far-off dressing room and called out, and if Father had just driven up, I could hear the various metallic clicks as he opened and reclosed the garage doors. Now, for a few hours, I would be myself again, yet not my naked self. In the evening I was more: I became transfused by my parents — the same parents I had scrutinized so heartlessly; all of me was quickened and added to by my father; all experience was intensified by my mother.

9

THE STUDY was the heart of the house. The room where the most happened; the one room that received total, unswerving respect so that maids never touched a paper, and the door, if it was closed and wore a small white sign "Call me at four," or "Do not disturb," was only knocked on in extreme emergency.

Like all the rooms in the house it was large and had a fireplace and wide, alcoved windows looking out on the lawn. In winter the sun was in it all day, shining first into the benign face of Grandfather Dwight, moving gently and gravely across the backs of books, the photographic enlargements of snowfields and glaciers, finally turning — at its setting — carmine as blood the binding of *Uncle Tom's Cabin* — the best volume with its little note inside from Mrs. Stowe to her new neighbor and cousin.

Except for some paneling beside the fireplace the walls were lined with books almost to the ceiling; books in Icelandic and Danish; books about science and mountaineering, poetry and art; a few rare and beautiful treasures like Cartwright's Journal of his trip to the Labrador. In the darkest, least desirable corner stood a desk for business matters, its drawers a constant disorder, its finish neglected. "That's a very fine antique," Father reminded us periodically, while the desk went on deteriorating, handles fell off and drawers stuck and were wrenched open. The real desk stood halfway down the room, facing the longest wall of books: an enormous island of carved black wood, flanked by racks piled with monographs and pamphlets, its top almost covered with its owner's written burdens — and joys. Until Betsy and I broke it, playing football with a pillow, it was lit by a brown china lamp with a Tiffany glass shade exactly the texture and color and iridescence of an orange jingle shell. At its foot lay a cast-silver ash tray in the shape of a bear flat on its back, paws curled over like a playing kitten's. Cigarettes rested between folds of its pelt and were ground out on its belly. There were lots and lots of these in the course of a day, their little heaps of ash almost indistinguishable from the dull silver curls of the bear's coat.

It was to the study that the head of the house went every evening after coffee to prepare lectures and correct papers, to write letters and speeches, and — when there was a little time left over — to write for sheer fun. A remarkable variety of subjects flowed out from his pen, in his even slanting hand: essays to be read at the Monday Evening and the Twilight Club, letters to the editor — these were not so surprising, but what suddenly possessed him to do a fantasy called "Is There a Man?" or a one-act play with heaven as its mise-en-scène and the "board of directors" as its cast? "As It Looks to the Angels" he titled it with a flourish, and years later this would be the title of a collection of such writings. Others, soberer and more reflective, got printed in magazines and discussed in many places.

Every evening that he was not at a meeting or there were no guests (sometimes even if there were) he sat there in his Windsor chair, the light from the lamp illuminating his balding head with the fine forehead, the proud nose. But every evening, no matter how much must be accomplished before bedtime, he did something with me. The books we read together, taking turns! Scott and Dickens and the *Last Days of Pompeii* ("Pompey two eyes," he used to call it, laughing), Jules Verne and Stevenson and Kipling. The sound of our reading was not beautiful, like Mother's: I stumbled over the long words; he breathed rather fast and in the wrong places, yet alternating with one another we made tremendous journeys through literature. Resting from reading we projected journeys of our own, the places we would visit someday, perhaps; the explorations we would make. He made anything seem possible, desirable; he made me feel extra alive.

How deep was his love for me! Deep and lively and open as the sea. How easily I floated on that dancing, glinting surface, lifted up by his laughter and sense of fun, smoothed and gentled by the specific feel and gravity of his look, his caressing "S'prcciousness!" as I came into the room and he looked up from his work to find me. Sometimes Mother joined us but more often she sat at her desk, writing letters to her sisters in Europe — the sisters whom war had made farther away than ever.

That last year of the war and the one following it were hard on both parents. He was reappointed acting president of the college, made president of a school for the deaf, president of the City's parks and of his university's alumni and was, already, a member of eight other boards. The whole city seemed to lean on him, yet at the same time he taught three of his four regular courses. After such full days he found himself still keyed up in the evenings, wishing there were something quiet he could do with his hands as I read aloud to him. He took up knitting: didn't the Prince of Wales knit? What was wrong, anyway, with knitting, with a man doing handwork? Though his fingers looked thick and clumsy poking the needle through the stitches, he knitted soldiers' mittens and mufflers which turned out as well as the women's in the house, and finding these dull, he went on to do socks. Turning a heel was a tense business: "Wait a minute Bubs," he would interrupt, and raising his voice call, "Olga! Olga!" first on two descending, then two ascending notes. The assistance she came to give was hardly necessary: the socks were fine, regular, firmly knit. He was still not satisfied: knitting was too easy; wasn't there something more creative, more fun? He could try crocheting, Olga suggested, so he went on to perfect that until he had made tea cloths for her and each of the sisters out of crocheted squares that he sewed into linen and finished off with tassels. There was only one more difficult type of handwork left: tatting. Now, under the light from the Tiffany lamp where he sat in his

Morris chair, a small celluloid shuttle flickered in and out of the finest thread, producing from his hands yards of delicate involved designs like unmelted snow crystals. All the guest towels in the house grew lacy borders; yards collected in the sewing-room drawers. He stopped at making lace: too hard on the eyes, he said; besides *something* has to be left to women.

When we didn't read, we made music in Harry's room, at the upright piano — he playing the clarinet, I accompanying him. He had taught himself this one winter at college when his roommate's typhoid left him with extra leisure. (It was a month before he could get a sound out of it.) Later he took instruction and was in a university orchestra, and since then wind instruments had become increasingly fascinating to him. One after another he acquired an oboe, French horn, flute and cornet and trombone as well as a whole collection of what he called with affection "my whistles" — among these a flageolet, a musette (which made terrible sounds) and an ocarina. Once every year all these went out to the laboratory, when he was teaching Sound, and he played Yankee Doodle on every one to his delighted boys.

The sounds we made could hardly have been very musical as we went through our repertory of favorites like "Juanita" and "The Londonderry Air" and Brahms's "Lullaby" — playing them *con amore*, I stopping at a rough passage to try it over as Father waited, Father — if he had let out a squeak or muffed a run — interjecting between notes an impatient "Oh, *pshaw*," and even stamping his foot with irritation. Sitting on the edge of his chair, his bewhiskered mouth pursed over the reed of his instrument, he looked like an ageless, carefree faun.

At the end of each piece we laughed with unbelieving joy and pride at having it all come out right, and went straight back to do it over again — to correct it if we'd made mistakes, for the delight of rehearing it if we hadn't. It embarrassed me that we weren't better, and I wished the clarinet's tone was sweeter than it was, but then I told myself he was not a professional musician and playing together was the greatest fun — a different kind of pleasure altogether from sitting alone with the door closed, trying to make the piano say whatever had been pushing at your heart. Perhaps he was embarrassed too, and that was why, when Mother came to the door to say it was bedtime or she wanted me for something, he asked hopefully, eagerly how it sounded. There was no way for *this* to come out right: if she said it was very good indeed, the pretense was transparent; if she just smiled and said little, the point was as clearly made. If only he wouldn't appeal to her for approval! If she just wouldn't be such a perfectionist! Years later when his duties were less, he was to work at it seriously and become the member of a small symphony orchestra and of a quintet, but at this time what we called our "musical orgies" often ended with a faintly sad echo as he wiped the clarinet and laid it away in its velvet-lined case, then — kissing me goodnight — said warmly: "Thank you, S'precious; well, we had fun anyway" — with a slight accent on the "we." His face was not sad: we understood one another.

No, there was scarcely an evening he did not do something with me, with that air of gaiety and festivity he gave to every hour of the day he was not alone. It was his attention did it: always right there — alert, quick, dancing like a flame from subject to subject while his rich memory and erudition and humor contributed a continuous glow. Nothing, in his company, was ever dull.

Then I went to Mother's room. She didn't do things with me the way he did, she just was. But as we talked, her animated glance and gesture and voice — that deeply interior and at the same time vivid presence — seemed somehow to make life grow. If I told her the slightest story of what had happened that day, the incident had a way of putting out leaves and flowers as quickly and magically as speeded-up movies of spring. It was never polished up as for Auntie Mabel, never reflected in appreciation only; a vigorous, critical mind went to work on it — pruning, cultivating, discriminating. Always cultivating! Ideas popped out of that ground; something I had just said (out of nowhere, it seemed) filled me with confidence and a sense of my own destiny. One subject led to another, Mother would have forgotten entirely she said time for bed an hour ago. She was still seated at her desk, uncapped fountain pen lying on a letter in her firm, round hand. The curtains were drawn making the large room smaller and more cozy than by day though there was no fire burning, for Nils — whom she inherited from Grandmother — was often stubborn and forgetful and she didn't like to ask him for wood. On the walls hung prints of Paris and Copenhagen; tabletops showed through eyelets of embroidery stitched on some Danish island; there were many books here, too: lives of Danish dramatists; books about the theatre and new discoveries in psychology — lots and lots of these. Yet gentle and embracing as the room was, something made me homesick there — what on earth for? Some other room? Just as Mother's hands — particularly the nails, so almond-shaped and delicate looking — appeared in need of pity I couldn't give, making me ashamed of my inexplicable new revulsion at the touch of her breast against me, the nearness of her breath.

"Aren't you two ever going to stop talking?" At Father's voice in the door we both jumped like culprits.

"Oh — Henry! Yes, of course. But you had her a long time too." How irritated, how miserable they looked!

Usually when I felt this, I tried to ease the tension between them, receiving from one, or both, a glance of gratitude or a tender, appreciative touch. That night (poor souls!) I rushed from the room and slammed the door as hard as I possibly could. Out in the hall, in the huge silence in which I heard my own fast breathing, and almost heard my heart (though not a sound from *there*), I gritted between clenched teeth: "I'll show you, I'll show you two!"

What was it I wanted to show them? That they ought to feel something they didn't? And not feel what they did? That they should pretend sweetness, the way Grandmother used to? I couldn't imagine. All I knew was that once, long ago, we had made a circle, the three of us. Now — how had it happened? We were three disparate points, separated instead of joined, it seemed, by lines of terrific force, as the three points of a triangle are held apart. And oh, it *ought* to be a circle, or so I believed in my terrible, young ruthlessness!

In my room, I threw myself on the bed. I love them so, I sobbed into the bedspread, I love them so! But I can't love them *together*, any more! I hate them for that — oh I hate them, I hate them . . . and I gagged my mouth shut on the terrible dryness of the cotton cloth and rolled back and forth as though prodded and pulled by pitchforks.

After a long time I sat up and looked around at the mysterious familiarity of my room. It hadn't changed! Like myself, I recognized everything in it — and I knew nothing. And beyond those walls, outside the curtains, windows, screens, shutters which the maid hooked together every evening and Fräulein unhooked in the morning, letting in the day — outside all this was the terror that stalked at midnight, reducing them to mosquito netting, to gauze, to nothing. Fire could devour them in a night. I could still see Betsy's house burning up years before: flames all blowing inward through black windows, then — at a signal invisible as that which moved clouds of migrating fish or birds — fanning with a huge roar outward, pulling the roof in after them with a soft and horrifying crash that liberated a sky-high fountain of sparks. By the time the last flames were squelched it was dark and only the street light at the corner shone on ruined, crisped maple leaves, into the steaming skeleton.

And there was the other, equal terror (or was it worse?) when, lying awake hour after hour, every muscle taut, I heard shingles creak, I was sure someone was in the room whom I must at all costs outwit. Once, in the light of early morning — most horrible! it appeared: a figure in the curtains beyond the Magic Closet. There it was, moving a little as it breathed, turning very slowly from side to side, contemplating each detail of my room, of my bed, of me. For an eternity I waited, looking back, then pressed the bell to my parents' room far down the hall. In burst Father in his old Jaeger wrapper, slippers flapping. He looked. "Why — why, there's nothing there!" he laughed, a trifle awkwardly, disconcerted. (Do you remember the time you thought you saw something in the curtains? he used to remind me, years later, with a laugh. Thought I saw? But I saw it: did it matter what it was?)

No, nothing was safe: one's room, one's house, the mysterious connection between one's parents. Those two! The two of which we are made, and who are two, no matter how much life and society, God and the church, impel them to be one. Is that why we are divided, each one of us?

10

A GREAT MANY people came to the house in these years and every afternoon, summer and winter, Mother served tea, Father joining her whenever he could, if only for a few minutes. Usually there was a guest, for this was the time of day people knew Mother was at home and that they could come and talk to her. She was a wonderful listener, to whom they wanted to disclose what mattered to them; often I was aware as I came in, or only passed the door, that some painful secret, just uncovered, still quivered openly in the air and it was just as clear, at departures, that the guest left with new courage and faith in himself. Sometimes she was as brisk as she had been in giving voice instruction: "I'm losing all my ideals," said one young man, bitterly. "If you're losing them that easily they can't be worth much," she replied with asperity; "it's high time you dug up some new ones."

How odd, then, when it was the other way around and I came upon a serene, comforting grownup and Mother

(*Mother!*) looking shaken and withdrawn! How was it possible with her wisdom, her assurance, that she could be unsure of anything? What could her friend (mostly the same one — a little candy-voiced old maid whom I called Aunt Lily), what could she possibly know that Mother didn't? She knew all about old Hartford — just who had married whom; that kind of thing and some vague and peculiar lore about New Thought, and the subconscious, which they discussed obscurely and at length. When Aunt Lily left it was Mother who seemed to feel better.

Someone was downstairs with her now. Quite a while ago the imperative rasp of the doorbell had sounded through the house, followed by the heavy, sucking sound of the door being opened and murmured politenesses as the maid took the guest's coat and hung it in the closet under the stairs. From my room I heard it all, even to the unmistakable little flicker as the string of brass beads which pulled on the closet light flew up and hit the bulb — as often as not winding itself with fierce abandon around and around the socket.

It took only a fraction of attention to classify visitors as they arrived. My friends called out, or whistled, and came straight to my room. If it was a salesman or one of those pasty-faced young men getting magazine subscriptions, there were, instead of coat-closet noises, heavy silence and self-conscious coughs, followed by quick footsteps and Father's devastating (though never unkind) disposal of them. "But I don't consider it the slightest privilege to subscribe to more magazines — in fact quite the opposite — and you, young man, if you spent less time reading them, wouldn't have to be doing this: you'd be doing something worth-while." For the unknown inventor, calling on the professor (only these always addressed him as "Doctor") with a sure-fire scheme for a perpetual-motion machine, there was a patient, exhausted boredom more withering than scorn; the stranger's voice — inevitably a queer voice that was either shrill, or truculent, or whining — trailed away in a bog of embarrassment. If the bell rang while we were at meals, it was someone asking for money. "Goll darn!" Father would say, pushing his chair back from the table, hands on his knees as he collected his thoughts, looking ready to pounce: "Goll ding it!" It was his most violent profanity; how could it sound so satisfying?

I sat at my desk, the arithmetic book open at a page of builder's problems, and listened. A man's voice was alternating with Mother's, but whose? A professor or student? A visiting Dane? Or just another young person perplexed by love or afflicted with difficult parents? Maybe just a neighbor and maybe — my heart jumped — someone like that fat Belgian with a passion for timepieces, who carried thirty watches at once on himself and moved about like a ticking mountain; or the gentle Russian inventor from General Electric who wrote such strange poems which he read aloud to us over tea. It might even be the movie actor Mother had discovered, and it *could* be the great Will Gillette whom I feared a little for his wit I didn't understand, but adored for thc way he made me feel so wanted, he and Mother exchanging looks whenever I was about.

Now I heard a great laugh and knew at once it was Dr. Ogilby, the new president of the college. There was no mistaking that sound, beginning with a gentle, reflective chuckle, winding up and up in volume in as unlikely a way as a donkey about to bray, breaking out finally into its engaging climax. It was impossible not to smile; Mother must be telling one of her stories. I went down.

She sat in the wing chair beside the fire, the teakettle on the table in front of her sighing and whispering over its alcohol flame, the tea turning cold in its cups and sandwiches untouched. She herself was a fountain of animation, taking first one then another part of the characters of her story. Slowly, as I dropped onto the firestool and helped myself to a cooky, I recognized where we were; the room became the steerage deck of an ocean liner, and Mother was a little old man from the ghettos of Warsaw — on his way to America to look for the brother he'd lost track of thirty years before. It was one of my favorites in the collection of her "tales," which were longer than anecdotes and had a touch of the supernatural, of the fable, about them. Dr. Ogilby, having gently acknowledged my appearance, had removed the bitten-up pipe from his teeth and was sinking further and further into a delighted crouch, elbow on knee like a very small boy, his nose growing sharper, eyes lighter blue with his increasing participation in the story being enacted for him. Finally Mother, giving proper weight to the curtain line, held up the imaginary visiting card to her hero's myopic eyes. "Mine Gott!" came the hoarse whisper, "mine brudder's name." And Dr. Ogilby sank back, making a wordless m-m-m, eyes gazing inward in recognition of life's incredible patterns. Mother leaned forward and blew out the flame; the delicate looking hands with their big blue veins busied themselves with cups and saucers and plates of food. The air was still full of her creation, of her — a beautiful kind of conjurer, whose skill with voice, gesture, pause, could make anything happen for us. I was most proud of her at these times; I lived under enchantment. Tell us the story of the elephant, please! I begged.

"I think you know that one, Rem. But I have a new one; about a ring!"

"Tell it, Mamoushka." "Little Mother," in Russian, was his pet name for her.

She threw a quick look upward, at the ceiling, as though recollecting. She folded her hands on her knees, and rocked forward and back once or twice before she began.

"This really happened, to a family in England, in Cornwall. They lived near the sea, in a great old house that had been theirs for generations. From time to time, in the course of gardening, or mending a wall, or repairing a road, they would find small classical remains, some Roman artifact. These things they collected and put into a glass-front cabinet in the dining room, till the cabinet became quite full with small ointment jars and potsherds, bronze hairpins, even a die with faded spots. But there was one find they prized above all the others. It was a terra-cotta plaque with an inscription on it, which — translated — went something like this:

Oh ye dryads of the wood,
Ye naiads of the wind and wave —
When will ye return the ring
That Cassius to his Julia gave?

They set this in the center of the cabinet and wove their
own myths and speculations about Cassius and Julia. Perhaps they were young lovers, or a devoted old couple, Julia
desolated by this loss of her life's token. But why invoke
the wood and water spirits? Had she lost the ring in
the forest or at sea, from a boat? 'Maybe she was mad at
him and *threw* it away,' said the youngest of the family."

(Dr. Ogilby's laugh fluttered in his throat, Mother
hugged her arms tighter around herself and went on.)

"Years passed, and the children grew up and married,
and nothing was added to the cabinet because life moved
too fast and other things were more pressing. Then one
weekend when the whole family was home, including the
newest baby, there was a terrible storm. All night wind
thrashed the trees and rattled doors and windows; rain
seeped onto floors in little creeping streams and the air
was filled with an angry roar. From time to time there was
a sharp crack as a branch or a tree broke.

"In the morning they went out, sadly, to survey the
night's havoc. The gardens were a ruin, old yews were
split and divided, and at the foot of the lawn, nearest the
sea, a huge, ancient oak had fallen. Its roots stuck way up
in the air and where they'd been was an enormous hole
that gave out the bitter smell of raw earth and broken
wood. The five-year-old grandson jumped in and they
all stood watching him throw up the soft earth and let it

sift from his fingers. Then his mother stiffened. 'What's that?' she said. 'What's what?' 'That little shiny thing.' 'This?' The boy handed it up to her. It was a ring. They took it up to the house and washed it clean and then put it under the magnifying glass on the library desk. Outside it had a design of leaves and flowers. Inside was written, scratched into the gold: *Cassius ad Juliam*."

Our guest had left when Father came in. Was he too late for tea? His tired face wore the engaging look of a small boy pleading. No; only it wouldn't be very hot: did he have time for her to reheat the water? He didn't; it would be all right as it was.

She poured it.

Reaching for the cup, hastily, thoughts elsewhere, he knocked it and spilled tea in the saucer.

"Oh *Henry!* Here, let me have it back." Annoyance swelled in her voice.

"It doesn't matter, really."

"But it does. You will drop it on your suit."

He sat there, sheepishly, a child with an irritated mother; as I watched, he threw me an amused, loving look. Then, between swallows of tea — horribly loud in the ominous calm: "Olga, did you write that letter?"

"Oh no, Henry; but I will, I will." The voice dragged with misery.

"But I told you last night it was frightfully important. I *wish* you'd do it."

"Must you keep after me?"

"But Olga, I have to or it doesn't get done."

Where had they gone, the harmony and music of control, balance, beauty? This place was all jagged with collisions and raw ends. It would have been so simple just to hate her for humiliating him, to hate him for — what? One couldn't hate him: it wasn't possible; and though my blood was set pounding by her tone of voice, one felt so sorry for her, too, as though at his entrance she was now in a wrong element, under wrong light. Like that pale gold moth I'd found in broad daylight, beating the powder off its wings against a bush, its face a terrible, fixed mask and on its wings a different face altogether. It was the combination was wrong — though that, I knew, was only part of the truth: when they were together something further was introduced — some error, or evil (there was no giving it a name) which preyed upon both of them cruelly — against which each fought and struggled, blindly and helplessly. The worst part of it was that they couldn't get away: they were two people in a cage.

But with friends — what a difference! They were different; the evil thing skulked away and hid. How gaily Father offered them sherry or the special cocktail he called "the Professor," which he poured, every time, as though this particular occasion called for the small, genial wickedness of alcohol and our guests, that evening, were the most important people in the world. And for the time they were under that gentle, amused look, actively surrounded by his kindness, and at the same time in the aura of Mother's charm, it was — for them — true.

Though he no longer wore a dinner jacket every night, he took great pride in the way he dressed and seeing him sitting at ease in his armchair one would never have guessed he had spent the day in the laboratory, the acrid odor of apparatus saturating his clothes. When I bent over him to give him a kiss a little waft of cologne mixed with his own good smell; if he was talking to a guest, he inclined his head toward me and with one hand patted mine, resting on his shoulder, holding it there in acknowledgment. Mother might be the most expressive and animated person in any group, but Father was so shining and held his head so happily and looked so at home in life that suddenly it made you glad you were alive, too. "Skoal," he said, lifting his glass, catching your eye.

In not more than fifteen minutes we were in the dining room and the glass doors pushed shut behind us. Our guests ate well. The cooking, more European than New England, was usually excellent for Mother took great pains with the cuisine; there was always wine — delicious, homemade wine when Prohibition came, with special, treasured vintages from the California grapes Father personally selected directly off the freight cars.

But the real treat was the talk. The arts and sciences, languages, philosophy and psychic phenomena were all eagerly discussed; neighbors and personalities almost never, for the house had an atmosphere as conducive to the play of ideas as it was uninviting to gossip. And play it was, never once that I can remember degenerating into argument, dissipating its energy in heat. How did they do it? It was the quality of their attention and the continuous presence of their minds: they were never self-conscious; they never withdrew onto islands of preoccupation. Sometimes Father anticipated what he wished to say next, thus forcing the tempo, and Mother, deferring to him, held back in the dance but it stayed a dance — the subject of conversation like one of those glass spheres held up on the spray of a fountain: revolving, bouncing, almost falling off then lifted higher than ever on a thrusting, splashing column. What difference did it make then if, when I was alone with my parents, they distracted me with their constant correcting of my pronunciation or uses of language, their nagging about table manners, their own terrible divisions? Now I was lifted too — held up on a fluid, sparkling, noisy rush of stories and quotations, laughter and response. I saw how they caught one another's eye. Life was never more alive.

Later we played games. The living room, by lamplight, had a soft bloom on it like the bloom of its velvet curtains. Mother disliked bright light so there was never quite enough — as indeed there wasn't in any house of that time when a single 60-watt bulb was as brilliant as a light could be. Because our games were mostly pencil-and-paper ones, we sat widely spaced, each in his little pool of illumination, pad and pencil in lap. Word games, categories, progressive limericks — all these our guests were induced to play, usually to their delight, though sometimes to Mother's and my distress, like bathers urged into the ocean in May. Why *does* he do it? Mother would then ask afterwards, her eyes, shoulders, and outspread hands raised in mock supplication. If we were tired of old games, or just if Father felt like it, we invented new ones. All these had in common the sharpening of memory, wit, senses — including his own that needed it so little. Games of luck bored him; his favorite became the intensely difficult Oriental game of "Go."

Spring and fall Father's best friend came to visit. They were alike, he and Father, in their love of life: "Uncle Carroll" had only to come into a room for the temperature of enjoyment to rise. No matter how often he referred to "this vale of tears" — his own eyes filling up with emotion — he spoke of life as a wonderful play which was, on the whole, more comic than tragic. And he adored the cast. People delighted him: people he knew well or had only seen once; people in books and on the stage; people he'd only heard about. He wove anecdotes out of the merest threads of dialogue he'd heard or incidents he alone seemed to notice — something absurd, or moving, but always intensely human. At the proper moment he told them, in a voice charged with humor or pity and arrested at intervals by a queer little catch in his breathing, like commas in unexpected places. His face was as expressive as his voice, his eyes — did anyone else have eyes like that? brown with ice-blue rims, like little sparkling halos? — his eyes like his whole face lit up with the invitation to share his enjoyment.

Father he regarded with a mixture of awe, affection and amusement — as though his friend's idiosyncrasies had been designed for his private pleasure. He had none of Father's physical energy and was fascinated by his friend's setting out to climb the nearest hill on arriving in some new place — in fact by his whole joy in discovery, his unlimited gusto. "No, my boy," he would say as if to a much younger brother, "you go out walking if you must: you'll doubtless go to Farmington and back by tea. I'll stay by the fire." Which he did — writing letters to his many friends, rereading a scene from Jane Austen, adding a page to his diary.

Mother, I think, puzzled him. Fond as they were of one another, they saw life in opposite ways — Mother seeing so deeply under the surface, Uncle Carroll thinking it wiser, perhaps, not to look. When Mother was in bed with one of her frightful migraines, he seemed embarrassed she could suffer so much — that such pain could even exist. "Poor Olga," he kept saying, "it's horrible — like a play by Ibsen!" And her "Ibsens" as they were henceforth called, like some of her ideas, made him both laugh and shake his head.

His own "dear Mary," as he invariably called her, was warm and gentle and unassuming — removed a little from the rest of us by deafness. At table she would often be left far behind, turning from one to another with her brow anxious under the carefully pompadoured hair, her mouth a little open as if to drink in what her ears could not. Carroll — who paused at such times to help her catch up, was her life: she sat watching him, beguiled, as she might have watched the son they never had.

How happy they seemed with one another! For the time they were with us I became their child and they my parents — parents with whom there was no conflict or shame, only love and delight. He had no profession: in the course of slow and leisurely drives between winter and summer homes, they spent up to a week at a time with us, the happiest and most festive weeks of the year.

Our reading aloud Uncle Carroll jumped into with
zest, and to witness his and Father's intense pleasure in
the book we were all three sharing was an intoxicating
experience. Arriving near the end of *Westward Ho* (which
he knew from letters we were reading) he was still taking
off his coat when he asked what was happening: had Rose
met the witch on the beach? Was Sir Amyas at sea? So
vivid to him was the memory of every scene he ever read
(and reread), so sensitive his response to an author, that
passages he spoke of this way seemed to be part of his
own experience.

This time something more happened. I heard his questions, I saw them light up his eyes and draw answers from
Father like sparks, and suddenly that other world of
literature revealed itself: a world as vivid as that of the
senses yet without any of the senses' limitations, a world
of unlimited dimensions. Reeling with the vertigo of discovery, I clambered up and down Clovelly's street and
stood in the bow wind on Sir Amyas Lee's ship — drunk
with the violent recognition of the power of illusion. It
was all a beautiful, beautiful trick! It was like that
other trick of so long ago when I found I could make
things happen in a language other than my own, but this
was incomparably better, for it had no limits anywhere:
it was as multiple and infinite and specific as creation itself!

It was dreadful when they left. Nothing made me so
happy as when every room in the house was being used,
each bed was occupied. At night then, in my own room,
I loved to sense the increased presences around me; loved
to wake in the morning with the prospect of more faces at

the breakfast table, the making of plans, the intersection of lives. What could be more marvelous than to circulate through a house so active, so fulfilled? To go from a kitchen as agitated and steaming with good smells as the pots on its stove to a pantry where special china and crystal was appearing out of cupboards and being handed down stepladders, into living rooms suddenly growing fresh flowers, and on upstairs, past the doors of cluttered, lived-in bedrooms? It was what the house was for, and when it was Uncle Carroll and Aunt Mary who had brought this about, my joy was at its summit.

They went. I turned back from the last blown kiss, the vanished car, to the ticking silence of the hall. Father was leaving for the college and Mother had gone to talk to the cook; *Westward Ho* was finished: life was over for months and months to come. I went to Mother's room and found her at the telephone table, alone, about to pick up the phone. Her face looked drawn.

"Both maids are leaving," she announced quietly, "they're packing right now."

"Oh — dear."

"Yes," she sighed, "this is a terrible house to run. Sometimes I get so discouraged I could cry." She looked as though she might. The house would be the death of her, she went on, and there were so many *things* in it! "But they're beautiful," I put in gently. She threw me a smile.

"That makes me happy! They're not all beautiful at all, but I have tried to combine them to the best advantage — somehow —" She waved a hand about, vaguely, indicating among other things the Victorian cheval glass, the

table and chairs that went with it. They were terribly ugly.
I'd never really looked at them before: all that cheap
veneer, the hard oval of the mirror's frame and the shelf,
like a bridge between its two towers of drawers: everything
about it was wrong!

"Grandmother gave me those as a *present!* And the
whole set to match! Never asked what I'd like or anything, just said, 'But you must have it, my dear.'" The
memory of it seemed to amuse Mother, in a sad way; she
smiled wryly. "That set and the few pieces I bought with
my own money for 'The Cell' — the little apartment I
had before I was married — are the only things that are
mine. Everything else was either already here or at Prospect Street."

"You mean you and Daddy never went out and got
things?"

"Never."

I thought of the yellow-oak bureaus she had had scraped
and painted, the great monsters of claw-footed tables she
had wrestled into different corners, the closets upstairs
that were crammed with unused things: all hand-me-
downs, all objects with a personality of their own which
was not hers, or Father's either.

"I'm sorry," I said, "that it's so hard to run. Could we
— do things differently? Or get rid of what we don't use?"

She shook her head. "It's no use. I've tried, but he
likes it exactly as it is."

I remembered the summer in the Berkshires and the
weary "It's your house, Henry, do as you like," and I
looked at her there at the telephone table covered with

lists and slips of paper, her worn and bulging address book bound with an elastic. Her hair was beginning to streak with grey, her face was getting that crumpled softness older women had. I couldn't bear it. A huge emotion unlike anything I'd ever felt rose inside me until I nearly choked. I didn't know what to do with it. It made the legs walking across the room, the arms I put around her as stiff as windmills. When I'd kissed her she didn't move — just sat and held me in her gaze and her eyes brightened and brightened and then she opened her arms wide. I laid my head in the hollow of her neck and patted her back. "Don't worry, Mother, I'll help you." For a long while nothing further was said inside the hug. Then I raised my head. "I'll go make the beds," I said.

11

BEGINNING or end: which was it, that spring? Beginnings are endings and so many things that year happened for the last or the first time, or slipped into one another as irrevocably as that imaginary line which passes from meridian to meridian around the world, saluted with church bells, kisses, resolutions, champagne.

"Arch Mitchell is coming. Do you remember him?" my mother asks. Remember Arch? The "prince" in *The Prince and the Pauper?* I could still say some of his lines, I think; still hear the exact tone of his voice. It is not the same thing. He has been in China now for years (like Uncle Edward) and has come home: how do I know who he is now, when I scarcely know myself? Remember him? Nonsense!

He came. A warm and friendly young man in his late twenties, full of an old and bewildering civilization, a temporary outsider in the new one: he was all uneven inside himself; outwardly, gentle and dear. He came into

my room where I sat at my desk, doing algebra; he sank
into my armchair, between the desk and the fireplace.

"I guess I'm disturbing you."

"No. It's all right."

Then, looking over my shoulder, "Imagine you doing
algebra! I mean, imagine your father teaching you. I'll
bet he's a good teacher."

"He is, but it's awfully hard — all those x's and y's and
things. Look at this!"

It was a language, he said.

"Like Chinese?"

We both laughed. Show me some Chinese, I begged.
He dragged his chair up beside mine and taking my pencil
from me drew some characters on a piece of scratch paper. I could hear myself breathing. What does it say, I
wanted to know when he had finished. He smiled, looking
into my eyes.

"Pretty young girl in house is happiness."

"Oh."

"Here, I'll show you my name in Chinese: James Archi-
bald Mitchell."

"What am *I* supposed to call you?" I asked as he drew
the characters.

"How about Jim?"

"Jim." I tried it out, uncertain.

"Sounds wonderful!" he said. "Now I'll leave you."
At the door he turned back. "No one else calls me Jim.
You're the only one."

For a year I had been growing and growing — so rapidly
I didn't know my own size, and broke things all over the

house in my clumsiness. How could they possibly break with such ease, I wondered, humiliated by them: surely I wasn't out *there?* Then one day I was taller than my mother, and Father, hurrying down the hall and meeting me coming out of my room, stopped suddenly dead and stared at me as though at a stranger: "Why S'precious — I can't call you 'little' any more!" My own father — who, since I had missed so much school after the Spanish flu was now teaching me daily, at home, seeing more of me than ever! While the most profound, interior transformation of my body — whose end (and beginning) had been darkly and fearfully prophesied for some time by the women in the house, made me a stranger even to myself.

Outside my home it was the same. Neighbors I had known all my life, and to whom I was as familiar as the laurel beside our front steps, began looking at me as though I had been away a long time, or I reminded them of something. Betsy's older brother, whom I secretly watched from the study window each morning as he walked by on his way to work, now took off his hat to me at church — me! I began to count the days till alternate Sundays when I sat in his family's pew instead of ours. In the spring of that year the older brothers even joined Betsy and me in our play, and the boy next door who had fallen out of a tree, and so never grew much over four feet tall, walked over on nice evenings to teach us "one old cat."

It was a spring of births. The cat in the slave barn had kittens; one of the neighbors — mother of four girls — had twin sons; our family collie had her first puppies. We

didn't know she was going to have them, and behind
all those curtains of orange fur they never showed, but on
the morning of April Fool's day — after a night noisy with
mewlings and squeals — the cook found them on the back
porch when she took in the milk. How had it happened?
"Betty" had been sent away to the farm for a reason not
clearly explained, but it never occurred to me to connect
the panting, woolly sausages my friends and I played with,
either with that or with what had taken place the January
afternoon before her exile when she had accompanied me
home from skating. I had tried to separate the two dogs;
I yelled and threw sticks at the other one but still they
stuck together. Some passers-by were no help, their faces
like masks. What was the matter with them? Why didn't
they *do* something? I thought the strange and indecent
and painful-looking connection would never end, and all
the while the dogs' eyes — at each end of the monstrous
apparition — stared, suffering and preoccupied, out of some
unimaginable distance. I wonder who the father is, my
parents speculated; I couldn't enlighten them.

Something else began that year, for all of us. Father,
who had been talking for months about a new develop-
ment in "wireless" took us out to the laboratory to hear it
for ourselves. Set up on a table was an irregularly shaped
crystal, a condenser made out of metal plates, a lot of wire.
Father bent over the contraption in deep attention, turning
the condenser plates back and forth, then straightened
up, saying "There! Listen!" He snapped earphones on
our heads and we heard faint singing, as thin as insects,
though unmistakably human. "What you are hearing is in

the Traveler's Building — at least a mile away." And there are no wires? we asked. None. "Someday you will hear across big distances, maybe even across the ocean." I was terribly excited, that night; the next day, very troubled. I tried to explain to Mother, but I couldn't: it was too big and strange.

"It's frightening," I said.

"What is?"

"That thing we heard. Sometimes I think we're going to find out so much, get so clever, that — that —"

"That what?"

"Oh, I don't know, I can't explain! That the world will get going faster and faster and faster, until — everything just blows up, that's all — just goes right off, into space."

I saw a great deal of my parents that year, being kept home from school and having all my lessons with them. I saw Father worn out and troubled, straining toward June when he would begin his first sabbatical in fourteen years. And I saw Mother laughing and teary by turns, in anticipation of the reunion with her sisters, of finally returning to Denmark.

How much there would be to talk about! She and Gerda had had their children; their first sons — born the same day — would now at last meet; Onkel Andreas and Tante Maria and even Morfar (Mother's father) had died; Ingeborg had married. Dominating these personal landmarks, brutally towering above every one of us, was the shadow of the War, which did not, really, recede. How could anything finished, and so apparently far away, go on affecting us the way it did? "They're so cheaply made

now — ever since the War," my parents complained, about
everything from new cars to underdrawers and "We have
to have *passports!* Imagine needing permission to go
abroad!" What was queerer was the ferment around us
which I sensed, through them, was violent and desperate
rather than releasing — as though I should celebrate the
first day of vacation by breaking everything in the house.
Why hadn't people been *happy*, when the fighting
stopped? Father went in to Mother's room that morning
and said gravely, "It's over, Olga," and she turned in that
little swivel chair in which she sat at her desk and the
tears ran down her face and both her hands went slowly
upward — as though with a life of their own — dropping
lifelessly back in her lap. "Now it begins," she said
hoarsely. Whatever it was that was beginning, Father
seemed to understand; he nodded.

Meanwhile they taught me: Ancient History, Latin,
algebra, languages. It was less like teaching as I knew it
than sharing with me what was familiar and fun for them:
I began to see that studies could be subjects one explored
with others, not only something one was made to do.

But how could anyone get so excited over algebraic
symbols? "It's so neat!" said Father, sitting beside me in
the Windsor chair in front of his desk. "Just look at this
come out . . . do you see how *beautiful* it is?" I didn't,
yet. The language of mathematics was still one I had to
translate into, slowly, painfully, blindly. Many tears
plopped on the green blotter, spreading into darker green
planets, during explanations. Many times I gazed out of
misery at the picture of the Icelandic women raking hay

— soothed by their quiet grace — while Father, with endless patience, thought up new ways to help me. Finally, in the spring, with no apparent change, I started to think in it directly: it was as magic as seeing in some design a shell or scroll that had appeared to be concave, leap unaccountably forward and be convex. It *was* beautiful!

Ancient History was baffling in another way. "Aren't they marvelous!" Mother exclaimed over pictures of Egyptian temples, and colossal figures with heads of animals. They were, but why? What gave such continuing, mute majesty to those great verticals, those round pillars bulging and fountaining at their tops above the widespread valley of the Nile?

At meals we talked about the forthcoming trip. After Denmark we were going to England (I would walk in real Clovelly! Maybe even into Doone Valley, to the church where Carver Ridd shot Lorna through the window!). Harry was to stay on, to read at Cambridge, and we had taken an apartment in Paris where I would go to a lycée and Father do research at the Collège de France, in the great Langevin's laboratory. He might even read a paper again before the Société de Physique, mightn't he? asked Mother. "On ne sait jamais," he shrugged, and they laughed about the experimental demonstration he had made last time, when Professor Henri Poincaré was there and bristled with questions. Do you remember how nervous I was? And we went walking in the Bois that evening, so you could sleep . . . That (turning to me) was when you were a baby. How sick I was of the phrase: when you were a baby. Now the *real* I would live in Paris, and Denmark . . . I would begin to catch up with my parents; I had already begun.

The time came to go. Preparations had gone on for months: trunks for Paris with winter clothes and boxes of Father's books; passports and visas, the lengthening of hems, the cleaning-out of closets. We went to my brother's graduation, and another commencement saw Father bustle about the campus in his academic robes, now topped by the new Doctor of Science hood. The fringe of hair at the back of his mortarboard was a little greyer, and thinner, but his step was — if anything — brisker, his smile readier than before.

Betsy left first, for Maine. With unspoken understanding we said little about the future. At the end of the year in Europe was boarding school; we both knew how much more than the Atlantic was about to separate us — how much was ending.

"I'll bet you come home with an accent or something," she said, swinging by her knees from a branch in our hemlock. Or — breathless between two cartwheels — "Promise to write me now; don't *forget*."

Write letters to another part of me? Not meet every afternoon to be together till nightfall? There is nothing whatever to say about a vacuum. It is, that's all, and when it happens, something, somehow, fills it.

She came to "55" to say goodbye that morning of the twenty-first of June, the first official day of summer. "I brought you this," she said; it was a collapsible pencil. "Look," she went on, taking it from me, "it shoots out." When it did, we both laughed uproariously. But already the future was separating us and communication was hard. "I'll walk home with you," I suggested. We walked very, very slowly, deeply absorbed in the pavement, blinking at the sunlit sparkles in the stone and the little wing marks of dust left by people's heels. In front of her house we hesitated, and she went inside to see what time it was. "I have time to go back with you," she said, coming out once more, the screen door slamming behind her.

For another few minutes, perhaps another hundred yards, we held life back.

Part II

1

✿❀✿❀✿❀✿❀✿❀✿❀✿❀✿❀✿❀✿❀✿❀✿❀✿❀✿❀✿❀✿

Sometime, I must clear out more of the attic — there's such a terrible lot of stuff — but he hates me to get rid of anything; he doesn't really understand about possessions, what they mean. Does any man? I get tired even thinking about all the things in this house . . . Sometime, when I go back to Denmark, I'd like to see Aarby again. Sometime — why haven't we done it? We must dig up that urn and scatter the ashes. Where can we do it, I wonder, and when . . . Oh dear, there's never enough time, and I'm not getting younger, and time is so precious.

I'd like to do an article on American Colleges today, but when? The book comes first; I'll get that finished and there'll be more time. And that one-act play — it's a marvelous idea — a lot of fun to do that. And (aloud) "Olga, sometime when Evelyn is here with the boys, let's drive out to the mountain. I'd like to see whatever has happened to the farm . . ."

They collect, the "sometimes." One by one, the acts to which they refer occur, in fact, and slip away behind like light poles from a fast-moving train or else they accumulate in fantasy: shadow-acts, shadow-plans, dusty with the regrets of not being realized, piling up like old china on dark shelves, like unhung pictures stacked somewhere under the eaves.

That was a long time ago (we say). What a snake of a phrase! Flowing on jointlessly, no end in sight, in the mind of the small boy hearing his grandfather tell about climbing the Matterhorn; coiled up — a live spring — in an older mind struggling to rid itself of arbitrary measurements, to make a little sense out of the mystery of time.

"It seems like yesterday," we say of years back or else, at the end of a difficult day and speaking of its beginning, "That was years ago." "Always," lovers whisper, and "never," and "forever" — lovers, the only millionaires of time yet as hard up as everyone else for time words. For time we have no language: forty-five pages of a *Thesaurus* cover all we have yet invented for it while for the intellect, volition, affections, there are five hundred and fifty.

Better, then, to say nothing of time. Tell instead how the little hemlock that was planted to shield the new garage grew higher than the roof, and ivy — started during the First World War — had to be trimmed from the top of the chimney; how the great oak on the lawn died and two fresh little maples took its place; across from it, the white lilac that was a gift one late Easter grew higher than the dogwood at its back.

Inside the house, too, things changed. The bedroom at

the head of the stairs acquired a second bed; the closet filled up with ball gowns, the soft and rustling ghosts of a succession of evenings. It became a guest room, then, empty most of the year except when, from time to time, a crib replaced the second bed and a baby pen was set up in the space before the fire.

In the room across the hall, framed degrees in electrical engineering and certificates of membership in honorary scientific societies were hung above the old upright piano. The piano was moved away from the corner and set along the wall: easier to dust that way. That room, too, was a guest room, its occupant away most of the year, designing radios and, later, television sets.

In the study, as always, most happened. Hundreds of slides, of temples in Japan and ruins at Angkor, of camel drivers in Egypt and pretty Chinese nurses on the steps of a hospital, collected in boxes beside the slides of Iceland and Denmark. After a kind of lull family photographs, and albums, proliferated: a whole album of a wedding; pages and pages of a large, blond baby against a background of azaleas; a little boy; more babies. Elsewhere appeared new paintings — watercolors, now: of Repulse Bay, a wheat field in Jutland, a cottage on Cape Cod; while to the musical instruments was added a beautiful bassoon, its separate parts kept inside flannel bags, like the best silver.

But these were diversions. The most important thing in the study became a drafting table at which the head of the house drew hundreds of meticulous illustrations and diagrams for a book on physics, while on the desk the most important item was the slow-growing piles of the manuscript. "College Physics," it was called; its writing, illustrating, making up (and solving) of problems, indexing and proof-reading, took nine years.

Nothing else stopped while the book grew; classes were taught and meetings attended as usual; an Icelandic story was translated and published, articles written and papers read. In a closet in the cellar, grapes fermented into wine, the wine was bottled and carefully labeled, in neat lettering: Sauterne, Château Perkins, 1929; Claret, 1931; while a notebook collected such comments as: rich, round, full-flavored, try these grapes again; (or) tart and cinnamony: why?

As the years increased, waste seemed to decrease. The man who had always moved without hesitation or uncertainty from one activity to another grew even more highly compressed, more authoritative. Yet he remained as merry and as extensively friendly as ever; no one, apparently, of whatever age or background or quality, crossed his path without being treated to that interested attention, that wholehearted laugh. Does the abhorrence of speaking ill of anyone at last cripple judgment? "Very much of a person," he would say to his wife, driving home from a party, about some obscure colleague, who, in the few minutes of association with him, had lit up like a rabbit's eyes in the beam of a headlight. Then, the fatal "Don't you think so, Olga?" and the incredulous "Oh Henry, no! How can you say such a thing?" making him bite a corner of his moustache and let the clutch slip in too fast. He would forever be baffled by her greater discrimination and worldliness as she would never understand the extent of his enthusiasms.

In her room little changed. Additional mementoes of Denmark appeared here and there; the books and pamphlets on psychology and metaphysics piled up. Evenings when he went to meetings or worked on the Physics text, she wrote more and more letters, addressed "Dearest Nickie," to Ingeborg married and living in Paris; and to "min lille høne" (my little chick) to Gerda, in Copenhagen. When another World War broke out and first Denmark, then France, was overrun, the letters stopped altogether: they could neither be sent nor received. And one day in 1944 an International Red Cross cablegram arrived from Switzerland: "Regret to inform you Ingeborg Curtis and husband died on November fourth and seventh respectively." Between Olga and Yvonne — the youngest sister and surviving twin — now living in California, almost no letters passed; they had little to say to one another.

"Ah ja," as Alfred Flinch would have said, and as she herself said more often, looking out from her bedroom at the copper beech under which lay his ashes, "life goes so fast, and how sad it is . . ."

Besides, a woman has so little to show for her life as it flows away behind her. How can anyone know what she does with it, really, least of all (perhaps) herself? It disappears, wholly, into other lives. The lockers don't fill up with writings, the world does not applaud, and the children — yes, the children — grow away and become strangers and feel (if they do not say it) an exasperated "Oh Mother!" They have to. Who, ever, is to celebrate, or even remember now what was said one afternoon by the fire at tea ("Then you'd better go out and dig up some new ideals!") or what excitement was planted in a daughter's mind, or what sudden understanding passed, faster than light, between grandmother and small boy desperate over an argument with his brother? They leave no trace, these things; no matter how illuminated, how vivid at the time, they are vaporous as jet trails at sunset.

The sun began to go down. As it went, the house grew harder to maintain; servants came, and left, and the repeated pattern of being unsatisfactory to their mistress, and being persuaded into staying by their master's pampering, built itself into a long, unsolvable war. With indifferent service, fewer parties and fewer visitors, the whole house — subtly and gently — altered. The finest ornaments, like the curiosities, went upstairs and were locked into closets: who, now, would polish a little silver sampan, or dust a box containing an Indian leaf beetle? But the chairs got re-covered and curtains renewed (for there was more money); more books got read and more fires burned, for the aging gardener, rheumatic himself by now, brought wood and laid fires without being asked. Slowly and surely the house grew mellower, nobler, sadder — the tenancy of its occupants more conspicuously temporary like that of hermit crabs, the house — like a shell — accreting more pearl.

The occupants, too, changed. But was it change, or perhaps, more nearly, return? More and more she returned to Denmark, in fancy, in talk, in judgments. About something unpleasant that had happened: "You would never see that in the good kingdom of Denmark," and "The terrible thing in America is . . ." The family resented it, blushes of hostility flaring up in the daughter, protests of "Oh Olga, *no!*" bursting from her husband. The worst of it was that she was so often right.

More and more, too, she talked to her daughter of the unhappiness of her marriage. The younger woman hated to listen, yet she was caught: being too young, at first, to dare say "I don't want to hear," and then becoming old enough to see she was the only rock on which these storm waves could break. "My mother is a foreigner, she is different and lonely": when was it she first suffered this knowledge? So she let the waves pound her as long ago she had let herself be overpowered and allowed the furies to escape onto her mother's bed. Nothing she heard ever elicited from her a detraction of her father — he *was* her father! Yet seeing as though under a magnifying glass the disease of the relationship, she felt sorrier for her than for him. Didn't he have his rich, full life? All those activities and people who needed him, onto which he could project his energy? While she who was such a deep well remained empty, unfilled, reverberating with hollow disappointment. "He's a boy, not a full-grown man; how could he be, the way he was brought up? That sickly, Victorian mother with all her sentimentality! I've been out in the world and I know. We don't really meet; there is no true communication . . ." "Oh Mother, I know, I see it and I'd give my heart to make it better. Would it perhaps help if . . ." and she made suggestions, recommendations. But mostly she just listened and consoled.

Side by side with this pain, offsetting it, was the increasing richness of communication between the two women whenever they met and talked of outside matters — the older woman's vision and brilliant intuitiveness making life shine for both of them in an unusually vivid light. Melancholy as she was about herself, she was as highly hopeful for humanity. "It's what the world is coming to, I'm sure of it!" she would exclaim — inspired and radiant about any indication of new awareness, or greater honesty between people. "We need more light on things, and finally we seem to be getting it. We're emerging from the miasma of Victorianism, and the artificial order of the eighteenth century — all this ghastly unrest and violence we are living through are signs of this emergence . . . just wait and see." When she saw in the paper one day a photograph of a priest, a rabbi and a Protestant reverend sitting down together to try to solve some problem, tears filled her eyes. "How marvelous! If only organized religion would forget for a bit to dispute points of dogma . . . the way it is, the Church divides people with its sects and its governments when it *could* be standing for the fact that we all have the same God. What else does the Lord's Prayer mean with its great beginning: '*Our* Father, who *art* . . .'"

"Olga, did you call Mrs. W.?" Despair creased the face at the dressing table as she saw him standing in the door: the finely expressive voice grew rich with exasperation.

"Oh Henry, yes, I *will*, I will, but must you interrupt us? I have her so little." Their daughter sat between them, silent.

Sometimes the clock was consulted: "But you've had her a whole hour." "What does it matter? You two are going to the concert tonight." Or there was an awkward pause and a laugh that wasn't a laugh. Each wanted her to himself; each knew that the other wanted her too. "You'd better go in to him now; he's so childish about wanting to see you." "You'd better not stay any longer; she gets so jealous." In the middle, shredded by the conflict and by her own love and hate, the object of their competition tried to weigh the imponderable, to satisfy the insatiable, above all to keep peace. Peace! So the victory went to the more demanding one: the magnetism was greater, the battle less. In his study the (apparent) loser — demanding nothing beyond these brief reconnoiterings, worked quietly at his desk; in the dressing room as the victor sat putting up her hair — more slowly and painstakingly as she grew older — at later hours of the morning — the two women talked, while at points of decision the daughter's squeezed heart made its silent protest: "But I'm not a bone to be fought over! please, please leave me alone." At home again with her husband and children she was sick with guilt for her resentments, miserable for the two beings in the big brown house — each one so remarkable, so beloved, but in combination tearing each other to pieces.

And with age his remarkableness grew. It became more sharply focused, more useful. Though he retired from teaching at sixty-nine, he was almost immediately recalled — in the war — to teach for three more years a greater number of students and for longer hours than ever in his career. He was seventy-two when he was made president of the Library and of the board of a new boys' boarding-school. Anywhere from downtown Hartford out across the mountain to Farmington and Avon he might be seen, walking briskly to a meeting or driving his antiquated car with its license "VOI." "Stands for Very Old One," one of his students quipped, and cartoons of the professor with his little pointed beard and his outdated car often appeared in the college paper. "Why should I buy a new car?" he would say. "It gets me there, doesn't it? And really, you know, they don't improve much."

Which was, in fact, his philosophy. The town he grew up in and served, the church he attended and the college where he taught — they all "got him there." Why fret about more? The world was a wonderful place, life full of delights and *they don't improve much.* To an excited telling of flying to the coast in ten hours, and of marvelous new throughways that would save hours of driving time — he shook his head and smiled. "It won't really save time. People will just go that much farther and more often." To other enthusiastic propositions for improvements he would question whether it *was* an improvement. Growth, yes, that it may be, but will it make people any happier — that's what I want to know. I still believe we are here to be happy." With the years his eyes grew sadder, the downward lines of resignation deeper, but whatever his unhappiness it showed in no other way; he was as full of fun as ever. No wonder, when at a dinner in honor of the Governor's Horse Guards he fainted dead away and had to be carried from the room, but returned fifteen minutes later, pale and shaken, to eat the dessert — no wonder cheers shook the hall! When he turned eighty, the Governor, unable to attend the festivities in his honor, wrote that meeting him had been one of the most "enjoyable" experiences of his career. "His choice wit" (he went on), "his broad cultural background and his unfailing charm of manner are precious attributes in a hurried age . . ."

The age hurried on, the old people slowed down, approaching the end. By what tiny steps (if we stay well) we move toward death! An unusual forgetting (did a vein close?); an inexplicable small accident — "Nothing serious, just a crumpled fender" (the response wasn't quick enough); a bad fall or an alarming weakness after a cold ("Your mother," says the doctor, "is not critically ill, but I think you'd better realize she will probably never be quite strong again"). For the child this can seem very nearly real death — perhaps even more poignant if less tremendous than the end of breathing. Those words "never again!" The dignity, and remoteness, of that face on the pillow — eyes closed, the veins at the temple so blue, beating so noticeably: *Where are you, Mother? where have you gone? (Run — go out to the garden, take a walk, do anything, anything while you absorb what he said! You, sparrow in the bird-bath, shaking water over yourself: my mother is old, old; she may die soon! You don't know about these things, do you? You just bathe and eat and fly till one day you smash into a window-pane or fall down dead or a cat eats you. But we know about death: we know we're dying and we watch others die.)*

There are attempts to protect. The telephone rings: "Bubs? Is that you? No — everything is all right, but your father had a bad morning — he was unconscious for a few

minutes . . . Oh yes, of course I had the doctor . . .
He's much better tonight, but his speech was confused all
day." And the mountain climber, the man who never
walked slowly, the man who at sixty-two had raced in a
four-oar shell, now walks with little shuffling steps as
though the pavement might rush out from under him, the
earth fall away. Yet his visits to his daughter and four
grandchildren still continue, and for the days he is with
them there is more life in the house — much more —
than at any other time in the year. Minds are sharper,
laughs louder; there is more music and game-playing; each
individual comes wider awake and steps more out of himself. Leaving him at the big station in New York after one
of these visits, his daughter turned once more and saw him
— taking those careful little steps, umbrella crooked over
his arm and the fringe of grey hair (thin and long) over
the edge of his coat collar. How rumpled he looked! He
who had always cut such a figure! There — he was gone in
the crowd. The uncried cry stuck in her chest like a bullet.
"Where to?" asked the cabdriver. No garden to walk in
this time, with sparrows going about their little sparrowy
lives; just faces, faces, bobbing along on the sidewalk,
secretive, absorbed, and an irritated, irritating man in the
front seat shouting at her, now: "Lady, where *to?*"

If they couldn't protect, her parents did prepare. Her
mother, though she never did clear out the attic, set things
in order, marked packages, put away. It was her father
who did most. In a handsome new notebook he made an
inventory of all the interesting and meaningful things in
the house, room by room — a sixty-six page document in

neat lettering (his hand was less legible now). "You have an awful job ahead of you someday," he told her, "I wish I could help you, but this will help, a little."

He took her about, showing her where certain papers were kept, how to open the safe. "I may not live much longer," he observed as though saying "I'll probably take the noon train." When she demurred he ignored it, and took out his key ring, clustered with keys. This was for his bureau drawer; this opened the wine cellar . . . "Oh — this one" (he slid it out), "see — it's a little bent and tricky to use. Here, I'll show you," and he made her open, after him, the locker that held the stamp and the coin collections.

One morning after breakfast he rang for Nils, and the three of them walked out across the lawn, still wet with dew, to the copper beech.

"You know your grandfather's ashes — your mother's father — are buried here. He wanted them scattered at sea, but somehow the time was never right and we buried the urn and it's stayed here. I think, sometime, it would be nice . . . I have always meant to . . ."

"Of course, I'll attend to it."

"But you have to know where. Nils — please tell us again exactly where it is."

Nils paced it out: six feet south of the beech, in line with the stone monument that marked a corner of the property.

"Have you got that?"

"Yes."

And they returned to the house along the lines of their

footprints, darker green in the silvery grass which — where the sun struck it — was sending up a little mist. She was thinking: How shall I do it? And where? But it seemed a long way off somehow and the thought was put away. Sometime she would get to it — sometime.

2

I HAD BEEN to one other golden wedding anniversary — a comfortable and festive occasion in a comfortable old house. The rooms were filled with friends; a string orchestra played under the stairs. On tables on the sun porch were displayed gold hollow ware and gold picture frames and gold jewelry — all shining hotly in the evening sunlight. On every available shelf and table stood vases of flowers: yellow roses from florists and yellow zinnias and marigolds from neighboring gardens and sprays of little yellow orchids with open throats and spread wings, moving as delicately as moths in the soft late air. On the bride's shoulder were more orchids nodding at each handshake, each embrace. Her husband went about, beaming; small children darted here and there with self-conscious expressions and shrill voices and icing-smeared faces.

The image stayed in my mind, no matter how different I knew the other occasion had to be . . . "We can't plan anything," said Father as the day approached. "Your mother isn't well enough." "Please don't do anything about it — I'd rather you didn't," said Mother. But they hoped I would come, and I came (with gifts) and my brother, who lived far away now and could seldom get home any more, sent his.

With me came the guest I had not invited: the image of how I wished it could be — not just the celebration, but the marriage: the ideal of Happy Marriage, which is so implanted in us all. Is there anything more rigidly inhuman? Less in accord with imperfect, human beings? It is the skeleton at the feast; to be unhappy in my world, was somehow to fail, and failure was disgrace.

We gathered in the dining room — we three and the family housekeeper who had come to us from Denmark thirty years before, Nils, and the old cook, and the nurses who now cared for Mother. She was visibly troubled by anything at all being made of the day, while Father was trying terribly hard to make it a success: there was some example *he* seemed to be holding up, some banner he kept flying.

What was it, really, we were celebrating? Not Love. Certainly not that spontaneous opening of one heart to another in vision and promise and life-transforming communion which was the beginning of marriage — its May flowering. How often would it reflower between two who for half a century sat opposite, walked beside, slept with the other — always this same woman, this same man? What, then, was its fruit? Concern (that was nearer to it); the wish to bring out, and be responsible for. (The number of times I had heard her say: "Here, let me help you with that lecture," or "Henry, are you sure you should?

You know how you get those bouts of bronchitis when you get overtired." And Father, refusing some invitation: "I wish I could, but I must stay home tonight; Olga isn't very well and I don't like to leave her alone.")

Nurture; consider; cherish — as you do the plant in the window or the seedling you set out, or the infant with a cold whose breathing its mother follows even in her dreaming. And in the caring comes attachment, and tenderness — the pang of remorse when the plant isn't watered; the leap of joy at its budding; the twist of the heart at a yellowing leaf.

> *If love means affection, I*
> *Love old trees, hats, coats and things,*
> *Anything that's been with me*
> *In my daily sufferings.*
>
> *That is how one loves a wife—*
> *There's a human interest, too,*
> *And a pity for the days*
> *We so soon live through.*

A pity for the days! With the days passing — faster and faster — the heart opens, opens (in how different a way from what youth is led to expect!) and something — impossible to tell just what it is — gets created in spite of the quarrels, or frustrations or despairs. An edifice is built, a house in which live not only the two who make it but their families and even, to a degree, their friends. Every kind of edifice, from the comfortable and orderly, to the ramshackle, to the one so ghost-ridden or patched together there is nothing left to do but tear it down.

Why didn't we tell the truth? Because truth has two

faces, one of which we want to keep veiled for fear of losing sight of the other one: the fairy-tale aspect (which is
also true), and which draws us into wanting the responsibility, into taking care and moving on — through what
territories — until, God willing, we come through. As
these two had.

That was what we were celebrating: coming through.
Could anything be more gallant, more touching than they
— in many ways so apparently mismated, often miserable
— come through to this place in their lives? What a pity
that like the onlookers at the parade, we made so much of
the Emperor's clothes! For the naked Emperor was what
we had, pot-belly, spindle-legs and all. It was human and
imperfect as ourselves, and oh God, it died, as these darlings soon would: how could we *not* care? What prince in
cloth-of-gold were we waiting for?

There were fresh yellow roses on the table, and a cake
with sugared ones: the servants had seen to that, as they
saw to and ordered the bottle of champagne leaning
against its nest of ice. Father drew it out, and the housekeeper handed him a folded napkin in which to hold it,
and as he untwisted the bridle Nils jokingly held his hands
up to protect his face. Everyone was smiling. Throats
were cleared in preparation for the toasts that each one —
all around the circle — made. For a few minutes, then, in
that room, as the old bridegroom filled the glasses and
passed them around, teased Nils and patted the cook's arm
and slowly lifted his glass to his bride — for a few minutes
out of time the banner he'd kept flying waved and flapped
for all to see. And she who sat at the head of the table,

in pain and bitter sorrow — one saw how for a few in-
stants she forgot what she had missed all these years in the
surprising feast of what she had had. It might not have
been what she wanted or expected — not that at all — but
this something else appeared to have its own strange richness, like the dark honey of wild bees. In spite of all, then,
they had created something more than my brother and
me . . . the house still stood; it was whole. Skoal! Skoal!

3

✦✦✦✦✦✦✦✦✦✦✦✦✦✦✦✦✦✦✦✦✦✦✦✦✦✦✦✦✦✦✦✦✦✦✦✦

BY TWO O'CLOCK night was over. A little east of the North Star, light began to transfuse the darkness and stars in the zenith paled. On the deck of the big, old-fashioned ketch reaching up the Sound toward Elsinore, figures and rigging showed up more darkly. No one had yet gone below. At four the ketch passed Kronborg, Hamlet's castle on the point of Denmark nearest Sweden.

Kronborg! Symbol to all Danes of departure and return! It should be Mother, not I, watching that dark shape grow slowly larger, its towers clearer against the lightening sky. I had seen Kronborg the first time with her, from the ocean liner taking us in to Copenhagen for that long-awaited meeting with our Danish relatives; it was my first sight of Denmark. Looking out my porthole in the unaccustomed quiet of the barely moving ship, I saw the low morning sun warming the castle's grey walls, flashing from its windows — and became aware of Mother's head framed in the porthole next to mine. Her eyes, fixed on Kronborg, were full of tears . . . It was for her that I was here again sailing past the castle in the dark this time, the dawn wind in my face. For her (it seemed) that one fierce white light burned in the seaward tower.

It was twenty-eight years now since she had been back. Several times she had been on the verge of returning for a visit and what stopped her I never knew. Was it her acute awareness of how fast everything was changing? On the last occasion that she nearly went, it seemed to me she was afraid of seeing what might be happening to the Old World, especially to her own little fairy-tale country. What did Thumbeline and Ole Lykoe, storks on thatched roofs and moats with swans have to do with this mid-century, not just here but almost anywhere! Each time a truck blasted its way down the street or a plane bored through the sky overhead — forcing its hard will onto sensibilities, into conversations — she shuddered and closed her eyes. It isn't human, she said. Perhaps it is this way in Denmark, too, she may have thought; and I'm too old to go now: my children must go for me. They must make my trip.

My brother couldn't go — he was too busy, but all winter, as it happened, my husband, our two daughters and I had been planning to cruise in the Danish islands. Our sons, as if following their grandfather, were — one of them, to explore in the Arctic, the other to do research in physics. Mother took the greatest delight in our plans. The Danish friend, a former Navy man, who was going with us and making the arrangements, sent us in the spring a chart of Danish waters neatly marked with dotted courses and little red anchors crayoned into our ports of call; on my next visit to "55" I took it to show her. She studied the projected cruise eagerly. We were starting from Fyn, not Sjaelland, she noticed: we would love Waldemarslot, and Langeland; she wondered if we would get as far north as Vejlefjord, on Jylland — it was so beautiful; she hoped we would see it. Just saying over the names of the places seemed to give her pleasure. The way she pronounced them, those soft "l" and "f" and "sh" sounds were as gentle as water on a quiet summer day.

But when May came, and June, we weren't sure we would get to Europe at all. Her eyes looked out as though from a cave and often as she walked — with a cane, the other arm supported — she groaned. Until eighty she had looked like a woman in her sixties; now five years later, she was white and soft and dry as the finest ash, bent by the arthritis that kept her to her room and the dining room and, on windless days, the downstairs porch. Finding her there dozing in a cocoon of rugs, her expression as absorbed and still as a sleeping infant's, was enough to make one catch one's breath, wondering if she had already gone. In the maple a blue jay cried; beyond, the factories hammered. Without warning her eyes opened, she smiled. "Must I go in?"

One could feel the emotions working in her. It was clear that she wanted, terribly, to have us go; she longed to hear what her granddaughters would think of Denmark, but just under the surface loomed the unspoken fear. Fear mixed with a kind of excitement — as though this trip we were making was to be as well her great, possibly her last adventure.

We went, in doubt up to the last minute about the cruise

itself. For one thing it was a summer of dreadful weather, not just "small rains" and quick showers but weeks of persistent, purposeful downpours with so few reprieves, let alone sun, that the current Copenhagen joke was of a tourist asking a boy when the rains had started and the boy replying "I don't know, sir. I'm only fifteen." All over Denmark, as all over Europe, the wheat stood dark and sodden and impossible to harvest. Outside cafés, the chairs were piled in corners, legs in the air, and the small round tables stood like toadstools and dripped. About the cruise our friends and cousins said either it couldn't possibly go on raining like this, or that if we insisted on going and the rains continued we could always come back and drink beer and snaps in a dry house like sensible creatures.

Then before setting out, our allowance of ten days was shortened to eight and we found the ketch was anchored in Copenhagen instead of Funen. We couldn't see why our amiable friend, Steen, was so upset by this: what did it matter? There was an estate over on Jutland, he said, and the family who owned it: he wanted us to get there; if everything went just right and we were lucky with the weather, there was barely time. He appeared to be under some deep necessity to reach the place. Tirsbeck, it was called: it was on Vejlefjord. Tirsbeck! The goal of a trip already full of meaning had been given a name. Before the cruise was over it was to become like the goal in a myth.

With a final delay on the day we were to leave, we set sail at a quarter to one in the morning — Steen and his wife; my husband and I and our daughters, seventeen and twelve; a crew of two.

It had rained most of that day, too, but when the red

light at the end of the breakwater slipped past and we headed out into the Sound, the masts gently rocked and creaked against a skyful of stars — the first we had seen in weeks. Steen was at the wheel, a square, bulky silhouette in a heavy sweater, a sailor's stocking cap on the back of his head. He was planning, he told us, to make straight for Kattegat and across it to Jutland: if we sailed for two days and two nights without putting into port at all we ought to make up the lost time.

Too excited to rest, we stayed on deck, keeping one another warm; talking as people do in the dark, softly and intimately; singing. Not until after Kronborg did all but Steen and one of the crew go below and fall into deep, exhausted sleep — so absorbing, so far below the surface that the steady battering of sounds, increasing in variety and intensity as the ship entered Kattegat — only pushed the sleepers into deeper layers of comfort. On one side, then the other, they braced in their bunks against the slope and roll of the ship. Under whichever ear was down in the pillow, water bubbled and gurgled, while the other was filled with the swish and rustle of waves, punctuated by creaks and bangs and crashing of kitchenware and footsteps running overhead. When — after a particularly long thunder and knocking of sails being reset — the chaos at once and completely ceased, I woke up; and came out on deck just as we passed Kronborg headed toward Copenhagen again and two soldiers on the ramparts were running up the sunrise flag. The white eye in the tower had closed; the castle looked exactly as it had that morning years ago, clouds flying over its vivid blue-green copper roofs and turrets.

What on earth? Steen, still at the wheel, laughed. It was just too much, he said; the weather prediction was for west winds of gale force for two days — and tacking into *that*, for forty-eight hours? "What are we going to do?" I asked. "Go around Sjaelland the other way: it is longer, but we'll be reaching. And if we keep going . . ."

We kept going. Past the docks at Elsinore, and Tycho Brahe's island of Ven; past the long wooded shores of Denmark on the right, the slowly receding line of Sweden on the left, till at midday we passed the towers of Copenhagen again and sailed out into the open water of the large bay to the east. There the wind dropped so that we had a swim — the only visible creatures, except for a few gulls, in all the endless, open afternoon. But right afterwards Steen ordered the engine started and we stuttered on down the coast — moving and moving until long after seven when the anchor chain finally rattled out and we found ourselves in the sudden, enormous quiet of a wide reach between uninhabited islands. No other boats were anchored in what hardly seemed an anchorage at all; the sun had gone behind clouds, leaving water, sky and shore the pearly blues and greys of Danish porcelain, and out of the north, what looked like a long black ribbon in the sky — blowing, fluttering, winding, unwinding — materialized into hundreds of eider ducks that settled on the water astern of us in a drawn-out silver splash.

We had covered that day, eighty-one miles, yet next morning the anchor was up at six. That same morning — when we once more headed west toward Jutland — another force than Steen's urgency added itself to us: the wind. For the rest of the voyage to Tirsbeck the wind not only changed and veered and contradicted itself (and every weather forecast) but as though with deliberate intent it blew from whatever direction would push us ahead with the greatest possible speed.

And the great rains stopped. There were still showers, but on the islands the wheat and barley stood up stiff and gold after its long drenching; garden flowers dried their wet wings; the cherries were ripe. At least once in every twenty-four hours we now went ashore. It might be at any time of day; because of our hurry it was never for long. Each place, already set apart by miles of water and hours of sailing, seemed even more its own small world for our seeing it at a certain hour, in one particular light.

Island by island, now, scenes of Mother's childhood became a landfall on the horizon; grew blond patches of wheat and dark ones of beech woods; materialized waterfront villages with houses and cobbles and people riding bicycles, the smell of a bakery, soft guttural speech. From our so different world we explored this one, connected only by Steen and his wife and the old black ketch anchored in the harbor. We studied the thatch-roofed doll houses, and were studied in return from behind windows crammed with potted geraniums; we looked into courtyards loud with ducks and geese; we met the village chimney sweep, slowly pedaling by under his top hat and his long load of brushes, sooty and white-eyeballed as someone dressed up for a minstrel show. It was all exactly as she had pictured it for me.

Once we went ashore so early that women were getting water at the village pump and no children were yet out;

another time so late everyone was indoors, at supper. In
one place, asleep under the spell of a hot Saturday afternoon, we strolled behind a procession of ducks on their
way to the village pond — "and there they met their friends,
the swans" — wasn't that what Mother used to tell me? A
whole family of swans it was: the father standing on a little
pincushion island in a bed of daisies, a single willow trailing
its arrowhead green overhead, while around and around on
the green-gold water his mate sailed after their four cloud-
colored cygnets — waiting for them as they investigated,
darted, dove or suddenly giving in to fatigue, folded the
black paddle of a foot against one side and floated among
the peaked ripples, half asleep. When our girls plunged
down the bank toward them she lifted her wings into two
spiked shells and the swan father, enraged, trampled daisies
underfoot and bore down on them hissing, swinging the
white rope of his neck. One almost saw on his head a small
pronged crown.

Whatever the time of day we visited the village church
— unlocked and immaculate, brass chandeliers bright with
miniature reflected windows — a polished silver bowl on
the baptismal font. Inside and out the churches were
white, white as swans, while the pulpit and organ loft
and sometimes the altar rail, too, were painted and gilded
or carved in full relief with flowers and fruits and full-
breasted naked nymphs. In one church the pew ends were
freshly painted with different common wild flowers (one
dandelion gone to seed) and in every church, suspended
from the roof, hung a model of a full-rigged ship. Was
Onkel Andreas' church in Aarby like this, too? No wonder,

Mother, you avoided New England hellfire till after the roast was carved!

We always bought something to take back to the boat: fish for our dinner, still swimming about ("In *Denmark* the fish is *really* fresh"); ripe peaches and cherries ("They leave them on the tree till they are sweet, sweet . . ."); warm pastry we tasted while still in the bakery. Then back to *Pan* and the waterfront boys fishing from the pier, or standing leaning on their bicycles, staring at our girls. Why aren't *you* talking Danish, their eyes seemed to say — you look like us. And the sails were hoisted and the jetty slid past and waves began. On deck, the older daughter picked up her book of French verbs, her endless letter-writing; Steen played his harmonica; the youngest one teased. And the islands — one after another — lost detail, ran together like watercolors, dwindled over the horizon.

We were nearly there. Once again we started at six, putting sixty miles behind us by noon, and again the daily shower drenched us but did not dampen spirits now high with anticipation. At the entrance to the long fjord on which Tirsbeck lay, we changed course. The wind changed too, brushing over the flat water in little gusts, sending *Pan* skimming past the stately farms and woods on shore, till late in the afternoon we dropped anchor off a deep meadow with woods on either side, whose long lines of perspective converged at the end in a brick manor house with one pepper-pot tower.

We went ashore. Up a half-mile avenue of lindens we walked, six abreast, under the tunnel of branches, in a confetti of evening sunlight, to where the house looked out across its moat — over the field, the fjord, and *Pan* lying at anchor on its own reflection. A bridge crossed water that was padded with lilies and swirling with enormous carp and very small ducks: one wondered which ate what. In the hall hung with antlers and brushes of foxes, a maid took our salty sweaters and preceded us up a circular stairs to the drawing-room.

How is one to explain the effect of certain faces, certain rooms? We meet, supposedly for the first time, and it is more like reunion; we have never seen each other before and we know one another through and through. This young, eager woman in her sixties, taking us all in with sharp blue eyes — blue as the fjord: who is she, besides being my hostess? A blood relative? The memory of an ancestor? Perhaps we played together once as children . . . hush, hush — pay attention: you are being introduced. And the room — look at it! My mother belongs in just such a room; it is so like her that I feel as if, all my life, I had been counting on finding it, had been homesick for it: those high windows set into deep white walls; that white porcelain stove towering in the corner and all these soft, faded greens of rugs and brocade and the pots of flowers — the whole as green and white and blossomy as a garden under the last snowfall of spring, and all of it watched over by rows of ancestors in great ball gowns and full-dress uniforms.

We were fourteen at dinner, the ages ranging from ten to seventy. There were, as there always are at Danish dinners, toasts and speeches. There was a lot of ceremony, and gaiety, no stiffness. "Do you remember?" (Steen asks his hostess) "the Navy reception you gave when I was a mid-shipman and when I spilled coffee all over a brocade chair?" "No, what happened?" "Oh, you *must* remember! You sat my commander — all in his whites — on the coffee, and led me over to the pastry table!" "Did I? Did I really?" Later, leaning forward in mock severity, she asked him: "What about the cigarette case?" Steen pulled it out — a silver one, with an etching on it of the ship he had been cruising on when first he came to Tirsbeck and their long friendship began. Inside was an inscription, in her handwriting: "So he couldn't pawn it in a rash moment," she added to my husband, on her other side. "You see, I still have it, Svigemor," said Steen; then lifting his glass, and inclining his head a little to give the look more gravity, more moment, he caught the lively blue eyes in his: "Skål," they both said — giving voice to the shared greeting, absorbing, as they swallowed, the wine of having met.

Next morning was flawless: a diamond day in which everything flashed or reflected or was a cave of color; in which foliage glittered with sky and a vine laid clear blue leaves on a white dog's fur. Not only was it the most beautiful day of the summer — it was the summer.

We rowed ashore and were shown Tirsbeck — the apotheosis of a Danish farm. Behind the old manor (built in 1301), the main farm community framed an enclosure the size of a town square, its long narrow buildings with their steep roofs of thatch including a head farmer's residence, a boardinghouse for apprentice farmers, a barn for a hundred and forty cows, stables and sheds. Beyond this the community extended up the valley of the "beck," or brook, which made the farm's electricity, and there was a dairy, blacksmith's shop, repair shops, bakery, fisherman's cottage, apiary. A mill ground all the grain, the great stones turned by beautiful wooden machinery, the whole building pervaded with the tart, powdery smell of stone-ground flour. Last came the workers' homes, pastures and vegetable gardens and a vast sweep of wheat soaring clear to the skyline where white puffs of cloud sailed out of sight. In the middle of the waving sea stood a curious tree-covered island. "Oh that?" said our hostess, "that is probably a kaempehøj — you know, a warrior's burial ground. No, they haven't excavated it yet — there are so many already in the National Museum. My mother watched one being opened once," she added.

What led me to discover, when we returned to the manor, the room with the drawings? In the living room, before lunch, I was all by myself. A gold-and-white clock ticked quietly on a table; the leaves of potted begonias moved a little in the air which swelled and emptied the thin white curtains. All around the walls I was being watched: shyly, or archly, obsequiously, gravely — a hand fingering a rose, or holding a book or resting on the handle of a sword. On a table stood a row of ivory elephants, their creamy ears and flanks glistening and reflecting like everything else on this day. I ran a finger along the surface of one: how could anything hard feel so soft; anything dry so liquid? Then my eyes were drawn to a little room I had not been aware of, whose door was almost hidden behind masses of plants. I went in. It was a tiny drawing room, all dark red damask and white wood and gilt frames — like a silk-lined jewel box — and the two walls which were not window or doorway were entirely covered with pen-and-ink drawings. They seemed to be by the same artist; they were done with the greatest delicacy and feeling: a sheaf of wheat; a doe and her fawn; a basket of flowers so piercingly seen that here was every hair on the underside of a leaf.

At lunch I asked my hostess about them.

"In the little salon? Those are my mother's. Do you like them? She did them as a bride — in Siam. She must have been very lonely out there, I think, so she took up drawing. After lunch I will show you some more — we have them in a book."

While the rest of the party took their coffee outdoors, she and my husband and I had ours in the library. Finishing hers first, she went to a desk and took from it a white folder.

"Since you are interested in my mother's drawings I'd like to show you this," she said. "My father prepared it for their fiftieth wedding anniversary."

She sat down between us on the couch and opened the folder, which contained a picture surrounded by a double page of finely spaced and highly decorated script.

"Read it," she urged. "He wrote it himself."

I could not, at first, because of the face that looked out at me. Between the elaborate curls and the elaborately ruched and ruffled neckband, a young woman gazed out with such ardor and vulnerability, such delicacy and determination as I had never seen. The tribute to her, and to their marriage was written in a style as simple and intense as the script itself was stilted and formal, written in a passion of tenderness and gratitude and love.

"You know," I heard her say, "my father was a very violent man. He had a reputation for having a terrible temper, and in his company everyone was scared to death of him. But this shows, I think, what he was really like, don't you?

"Tell me about *your* mother," she said abruptly, jumping to her feet and putting the folder away. "She's Danish, isn't she?"

I told her how she had gone to the States, yet how Danish she had remained; how much this trip of ours with her granddaughters meant to her. When I had finished, the blue eyes widened and she jumped to her feet.

"I have a present I would like you to take to her. From one Dane to another." She brought a huge book and laid it on my knees. It contained all the drawings her mother had done, reproduced down to the finest line on heavy, rich paper, beautifully bound. The family had had a few of these made, she said, and they represented her mother's work from her first drawing as a girl of sixteen through those she had done in her old age — most of the latter ones Danish scenes: churches and gardens and farms as well as her favorite wild flowers. Such a present it was that I was not sure I had heard correctly, but the great book was pressed into my hands when we left, the message repeated.

It seemed impossible to leave. In the garden we walked more and more slowly beside our guide as she talked and picked a flower here, another there, "for a farm bouquet that you can take on the boat." On the lawn beyond the moat, the young people lay sprawled with lots of cushions, and the golden afternoon grew more still, more golden, as though the whole summer condensed at the last into a perfect crystalline globe of a drop which would never break, never fall.

But then our host came back from inspecting cattle, his ill-tempered Sealyham at his heels, a maid announced tea, and everyone ate too much fresh bread-and-butter and cake and it was time to go. The lady of Tirsbeck walked down to the fjord with us and out to the very end of the narrow, rickety dock where she stood waving a large white handkerchief as our anchor came up. When we started to bear off, she parodied her own farewell and turned slowly back and the long tunnel of lindens swallowed up the little figure in the bright blue dress. On *Pan* we dipped the flag three times and spread out the chart.

From that moment on the summer declined — as though a play were over and the curtain had fallen. Even before we sailed out of the fjord, the sky clouded over, and with the exception of one unnaturally hot day the following week, we never again had a single pure day of summer that year. For the rest of the cruise there were gales and squalls; the water was the color of slate or else a wild grey-green raked with claw marks of foam; in the sky an endless battle of clouds was waged in different formations and layers and depths, with only a rare opening through into blue — clear and serene as those cloud windows on chapel ceilings from which round faces framed in wings peer down.

On deck we wore slickers and got lame muscles from fighting the wheel. In the cabin, everything movable slid and banged and fell and the vase with the farm bouquet kept tipping over, streaming water onto the floor. Braced in a corner, the daughter who had been writing to school-mates and boys all summer now wrote a letter to her grand-mother. "Oh, I am so proud of being one quarter Danish," it ended. And the younger one, bent way over the table, hair in her eyes, did a careful watercolor of a Danish farm — half-timbered stucco, thatch roofs and all; it took her a whole morning to get the proportions of roofs and buildings and courtyard right. Back in Copenhagen again, we air-mailed the letter and the picture to their grandmother. The book, because it weighed so much, we took to an agent to have shipped.

Three weeks later we were home and in less than twenty-four hours, I was sent for: my mother was sinking. I came into the room fearful of what I should find, but there was no apparent cause for alarm: she seemed un-diminished, her smile undimmed. "So the girls loved Den-mark," she said; they were her first words. "Look!" She pointed to the mantel where the picture stood propped. "And these," she went on, indicating their letters on the bedside table. She made me read them to her although she knew them by heart. So perfect was her performance (and I think it was that) that I began to wonder why I had been sent for so quickly, but later in the day I saw how her strength was ebbing. "Tell me about Denmark," she whis-pered, "everything." She lay with closed eyes while I sat beside her, talking, and I would think she had fallen asleep until — if I stopped — she opened them, saying "And then?" She wouldn't let me leave anything out.

I had postcards of Tirsbeck. At the sight of the old

brick house with its pepper-pot tower, a delighted, sighing
"Oh, *yes*" came out of who knows what memories. "I
stayed in a place like that," she said, very faintly. Her chin
trembled. And here (I showed her, on another card) is an
air view: see this is the farm, around that square, here are
the barns, and the sheds; the duck pond is there. Is that
my voice talking? Or hers, long ago? Which is the mother,
telling a story, and which the child, listening, on the verge
of sleep? I picked up the hand with its blue ropes of veins,
its third, fourth and fifth fingers so bent under from a life-
time of picking up and handling and putting down that
there was almost nothing left to hold — and I held it, and
I told her the story of Tirsbeck. When I came to the part
about the book her eyes flew open, tears running from the
corners, and she looked not at me but at something I could
not see, somewhere in the air above her — not vacantly or
glassily, but as an infant will stare sometimes — intently
and long and scarcely breathing.

"How lovely, how *lovely!*" she whispered. And then, so
low I could barely hear, "It is as though her spirit had
reached out to me — across space, across time, and given
me her hand." What was her name, she asked me. My
answer conveyed nothing; I remembered only that the first
name was Maria.

Two days later came a notice from the U. S. Customs
Service — item: one book. I got on the phone; I reached a
chief inspector: couldn't they please cut red tape, I begged;
I would do anything possible to expedite the book's release
and I gave the reason. How dry the words sounded: my
mother is dying; the book is a gift; sentimental value only.

All so much paper in the air — not even to be impaled on one of those spikes on an official's desk! Just another voice on the telephone, though a somewhat constrained and distressed one. Yet I thought I detected *something* in the mumbled reply, and I believe he tried — whoever he was — for the book came soon.

It was not soon enough. Three days later Olga Flinch died. Was she, in her last hours, reconciled to her two lands? Can one be, ever? Once, her hands passed gently over the bed-head, the table edges on either side of her, caressing them, and she murmured, "Familiar things, all familiar things." But the night she died she sang a Danish song. And every night after I came home she said the same thing to her young Estonian nurse — another displaced soul, displaced by war: "A beautiful thing has happened, Lydia. Listen. I am going to have a wonderful present . . ."

4

I LOOKED up at the house. In the open window of the sickroom the triangle of a white cap set on dark hair went
slowly back and forth, back and forth with its wearer's
rocking. Vines were beginning to touch across the window: I must get them cut. Everything was growing so fast
— the cedars at the dining-room windows, the laurel and
rhododendron creeping out across the front walk, brushing
you as you walked up to the front steps — the forsythia
advancing in solid, leafy phalanxes across the lawn. Soon
the whole house would be engulfed in tides of green while,
inside, the old man slept his life away.

It was the Fourth of July, nearly two years after the Danish cruise; for the whole last year my father had been bed-
ridden, his house a hospital. At home, friends had asked
me if we would join them at the annual Independence Day
Dance. "You're not coming? . . . But it will be a good
party! . . . Why not? . . . I'm going to visit my father,
he's very ill . . . Oh, poor you . . ."

There was no need for pity. The day presented me with that greatest wealth one can be given in mid-life: time. A great big room of it — twenty-four hours multiplied by another, nameless dimension into an immeasurable space.

And it was quiet. Factories were closed for the day: no banging; few cars went through our street; there were no firecrackers. All day one heard a wood thrush in the garden, making his delicious, random-sounding experiments with melody, in a slow lingering tempo. He had room, too. The telephone never rang; I called no one. My car stayed locked in the garage — the dragon chained down. Undriven, uninterrupted, emptied of all purpose, I heard the least thing speak to me.

The twelve months preceding this had been a fantastic and terrible journey, repetitive as dreams in a fever. Exactly a year before, between daybreak and noon, whatever thread it is on which our thoughts are strung snapped in my father's mind. That mind! What an abominable joke! One day, he had spoken the first twenty lines of the *Iliad*, in Greek, shaking his bald head, tears in the sad old eyes — "Isn't it *marvelous*," he said. A week later, eyes lost, one corner of his mouth pulled down and out of control, he sat plucking at his frayed wrapper cord, babbling nonsense. "Are you warm enough?" we asked. No answer. "Can I do something for you?" "That's a bird of paradise under the tree — catch him! catch him!"

He's not suffering, we consoled ourselves, yet how does one know? Perhaps the question is understood and a bird of paradise flies out in place of an answer. One can only pray for a quick release, and several times that summer it seemed he would have it. Once, when I had been sent for and arrived in the night-long siege of roaring rain following a hurricane, we were isolated by floods even from the doctor, but in the room on the other side of the wall from mine, the terrible breathing evened out, grew less loud, and by morning a little more life flowed back.

Each time I was in his room there was the same effort to meet him, and communicate somehow, something. Each time might be the last, and he always knew me — greeting me with one of the special nicknames he had for me, his sunken face transformed in a radiant smile. How easy it was to return the endearment: kiss the wry mouth or the clammy forehead, tell him I loved him! With all life's pressures gone, how open and simple love becomes . . . And one can communicate with a wandering mind; it is a different world, that's all, rather like the world of children's games. It has its own rules. You must be willing to be anywhere — the jungles of Indochina, Sherwood Forest, the Opera in Paris; you must pretend: the washcloth is a handful of tickets ("Are the seats all right? Can you see?"). You must admit the dead, who are not dead: "Olga, Olga!" (on two descending notes, then two ascending) and Nils, the gardener, who died last year, and Aunt Nickie, and — it hardly seems possible — Mary Evelyn, his own mother. I explain they are not here and he gets annoyed with me: "Not here? all sorts of people have been disappearing lately; you're hiding them from me." Sometimes he is very funny, mischievous as a boy, eyes dancing, and we all laugh like fools at the bedside, the nurses and I, and he as loudly as the rest.

But mostly, that first summer, the nurses fought. Across the bed with its stertorous sleeper, wetting and soiling the sheets, crying out like a child in a nightmare, they bickered and denounced and jockeyed for position, plotting to humiliate one, defending another, and always storing up their miseries and hatreds behind the dam of my absence. On my arrival, often till late into the night, the foul waters escaped: "See, see what she does!" one would hiss, while another — coyly, sparkling with innuendos, whispered, "I don't suppose it's my business, but —"

I fired them all, the apparently innocent with the clearly guilty: the air was too polluted for innocence. New nurses came, throwing open the windows, removing straps from the patient the others had found necessary, admitting love. No one was to say a word about the sick man in his presence: "We have no idea what the sick hear, even in coma," they said firmly. The house filled with warmth and light again. The maids sang.

Once more I went home to husband and children as I had been doing over and over for months — to open mail and throw out pounds of advertising; run my house; pick up the phone when it rang and listen to an earnest voice saying: "I don't think we should ask Marian, you know she and Gladys have never liked one another, *really*, and besides you know what she said at the last meeting . . . You weren't there? Oh I forgot, you were away . . ." When she finished, I sat for a long time staring at the instrument lying in its cradle, equally capable of letting us vault over deathbeds or beds where couples are making love and we none the wiser. Yes, I had been away.

But all that was last year. When I came this July it was to a peaceful, sunny plateau, the invalid enough better so that he enjoyed the small pleasures of an occasional cigarette, a postcard from a friend. He wanted to hear about his grandchildren and even asked me to read to him. The nurses loved him and his disposition was unchanged: he beamed with smiles; he corrected their English.

Once more the house had changed, this time into a state of the utmost serenity. In the empty study sunlight moved from one window to another, across the backs of books and over the Icelandic women raking hay, glinting on the little upside-down bear who no longer received ashes; next to it in my old room, the elderly housekeeper in her spare time sat at a frame making hooked rugs. Upstairs and down, cleaning, carrying trays, helping in the sickroom, went redheaded Mary, the housemaid, in her gym sneakers, laughing and singing to herself; once a week Mother's Danish maid came to keep things as her mistress would have liked, bringing flowers for the bedside from her own garden. And every hour of every day the nurses, in rotation, cared for their patient with hands and hearts and imaginations. If the enormous vitality that had been my father had shrunk to one room, into one bed, the house, now, was entirely free of stress, everyone in it dedicated to the same end. The life of the house had become a child, loved and cared for by three mothers — seven, if you counted us all.

That morning of the Fourth of July, he was indignant with all his mothers. It was wrong, he said, to try to tell him this was home when it wasn't. "Where is it?" I asked. "Why — don't you know?" (His head turned on the pillow, he looked at me in astonishment) "It's a hospital." But isn't it odd, he added, that the disposition of the rooms is the same, indicating with his head the locations of doors and windows. It was. It was even odder that — as so often happened — his "hallucinations" were more like truth with appearances rubbed away. A moment later he was asleep and snoring.

In the next room I wrote to Betsy — Betsy, with whom, after years of having gone our own ways, not even sending cards at Christmas, there was again a deep friendship. Or, rather, a new friendship seasoned by the childhood one, for it was completely fresh and devoid of dead loyalties. She still loved the house, my father, me; she dreaded the death of the house and the task it would entail and had now offered her help when the time came. "I won't bring it up again," she had written; "just remember I'm here." It was a long letter I wrote in reply — our secret writing place a few feet away. Ghosts of the past became animated by the present and when I had finished, the great wound of time felt clean, almost healed over. We had not, after all, been totally abandoned by those two little girls behind the piano.

When I returned to the sickroom, the small ceremony of Father's daily wineglass of half whiskey, half water, which he called his toddy, had already begun. Flushed from sleep and propped up against the pillows, he looked very nearly himself except for that mysterious shrinkage of old faces, the subsiding fire in the eye. The glass was in his hand, the nurse on the far side of the bed standing ready to guide it when necessary. Together we watched the snail-cautious progress of the waxy, unused fingers bringing the liquid to his mouth: in the room's midday brilliance the drink shone like a topaz; one could see the tiny tightening of anticipating lips. He had never lost his attitude that drinking was slightly risqué; now with the glass halfway, he turned to the two of us and with a mischievous, conspiratorial look: "Booze," he said naughtily — and noticed I had none. "Here, take mine," he urged, brow furrowed with distress, and nothing would do but that Mary should bring me a toddy, too. By the time she had returned with her swinging, loping walk, her beaming face, the giving of a midday stimulant to a sick old man had swelled into an occasion.

"Your father has been telling me about the cats of Beacon Hill," Mrs. Dawson said. She leaned over him and laid her hand on his shoulder. "Can you tell us again?"

"Let's see." He began to recite a long piece of light verse. Sometimes he hesitated or faltered at a rhyme, went back and started over. On either side of the bed we listened and encouraged, until he came to the end and laughed a delighted laugh. We exchanged looks: she was shiny with the pleasure of the confident mother who can count on her child.

"Do you remember the Jumblies?" he asked. I fetched the book from the empty study and read the poem aloud, the pictures of the ridiculous Jumblies waving happily to me from the page. At each chorus —"Their heads are green, and their hands are blue, and they went to sea in a sieve"— he tried to join in and we all laughed.

It had become a party. Outside the window, the maple

leaves hung motionless, waiting; the wood thrush improvised. In the room the three of us (dare I speak for
him too?) floated in peace and timelessness and undemanding love. Father, mother, child — the eternal trinity
— how strangely dissolved now and recombined, like something seen through water: the father become child; the
child become parent; another, unattached mother embracing them both. For her presence was embracing, and the
occasion itself a fluid in which other past occasions and
incidents — as set and hard as crystals — melted away.
This neutral mother loved my father and demanded nothing of me. This dying father — to whom, in the absence
of all conflict, all jealousy, I could finally express my love
— had been requited at last. The terrible triangle had
been broken. I was redeemed.

"It's good," he said, "don't you like it?"

"Like what?" I asked, startled.

"Your toddy."

"It's delicious."

His glass was near his lips, but he hesitated, holding it
where it was. He caught my eye. "Skoal" he said. With
the pillows at the angle they were he couldn't incline his
head. Still he didn't drink; he was trying to think of something. Then he said a Swedish toast — loud and strong:
"Min skaal! Din skaal! Alle vackere flicke skaal!" (Here's
to me, here's to you, here's to all the pretty girls.)

A few minutes later he was insisting that sixty people
were coming for dinner — would I please see to the wines?
And lunch was announced.

Later I went outdoors and strolled about. A rabbit, startled by the screen door closing, hopped away a few paces, but made brave by curiosity, never vanished into the bushes — just hopped ahead of me all the way around the lawn. In the house next door, I knew the children of the family had collected today to distribute their mother's belongings; she had died two weeks ago. Now I heard their voices leaving her house, moving across her lawn to where the eldest son lived in the Gillette house. Behind the wall of rhododendrons between the two places passed the jigsaw pieces of their figures: a white shirt, a scrap of blue, a crescent of head. Then they all passed into the other house, last Henry — the short one who had fallen from a tree — and the door banged behind them.

At the copper beech I stopped, and the rabbit stopped too, a little way in front. The ground on two sides of the tree was scarred up from digging, raw brown, uneven. It was beyond believing: the urn hadn't been found. The new gardener got in a helper; they widened the excavation. Still nothing. If the urn was not of bronze, I was told, it could have disintegrated, but there was no one left alive who knew, who could tell me. What was to be done? I had promised Father to take care of it — and, more important, Mother's last wish was to have her ashes scattered at sea together with her father's. Poor displaced souls! Daughter following father to the new country neither really cared for, both wishing to end in the sea that divided them from home, the daughter following her father even in death.

Not to leave anything undone, we had stopped on our way to the seashore with the children in the car, to have a look for ourselves. While my husband walked the dog, I went to the open trench and jumped in; I even did some digging myself: it *must* be there! — looking out from time to time over the piled-up earth at the puppy pulling his master around the lawn. The tears that had been gathering — of loss, and pity for the dead, of vexation for what was expected of the living — turned abruptly into tears of laughter. I laughed and laughed. How hopelessly gravity and absurdity were mixed up! There in the car were my mother's remains — hidden, to protect the children, in a hatbox; there, on the lawn beyond the grave's edge, my husband watched hopefully for the puppy to lift its leg; here in the open grave stood I, trying to find what was left of my grandfather. Alas, poor Yorick! Alas, poor Alfred, your ashes lost in foreign soil; made, in spite of yourself, to add to that soil. "The trouble with America," you used to say, "is that it hasn't yet enough dead."

The day moved peacefully toward night until, when it was finally dark, fireworks began over in Pope's Park. From the sleeping porch beyond the sickroom, the aerial ones were clearly visible, the Catherine wheels and red fire lit up the air from below. At the first stunning bangs of aerial bombs, the night nurse shut the windows, but though she and I both flinched, the patient snored on. Then came the rockets — with their showering fountains exploding into light and sound, spraying out into long, slow falls, and after each burst a long-drawn-out Ahhhh mixed with the rattle of people clapping, like the rattle of approaching rain. Pffutt! went each new one, the tourbillions twisting dizzily as they gathered speed, until light exploded into more light shimmering like Christmas tinsel, going on and off, appearing to defy gravity, until slowly — how slowly — it began its return to extinction. Another wiggled up into the dark — a light-freighted spermatozoon — and burst into being, into flower. I *am*, declared the light, shining and sparkling and expanding in the air into more and more light, until one by one the flowering sprays changed direction, softened, weakened; were drawn back into the darkness and vanished.

My back against the wall of the house, I watched, heart pounding. All day something was being shown to me, culminating now in excitement beyond conscious understanding. What was it? You are still the child, was what morning had said: no matter what has happened since, you and the little girl behind the piano are still one and the same. And this is you, too, noon told me at the bedside: you must go through this disintegration — in your own way, your children powerless to help you. And this is where it ends, said the broken-up earth at the foot of the copper beech. But the fireworks were challenge and promise — both. Between the dark and the dark they burst — one out of the other, seed into flower into seed — a vision of being itself, pure being expressed in light. BE! said each rocket, boring its way up. FREE! commanded the multiplying light, exploding outward, out . . . And my heart, ahead of mind and time and experience, answered for me.

5

"BUT I'm afraid your brother is asleep, Dr. Perkins," said the nurse. "Never mind," replied Edward gently, "I won't disturb him. I'll just sit."

And having been helped to the sickroom, there by the bedside he sat — half an hour, an hour — the shapeless lump of his body making big folds in the spotted suit, the calm, childlike eyes gazing out from his sagging head, never veering from the grizzled object of his adoration. In an armchair by the window sat Georgie, half asleep in her Scottish shawl.

Uncle Edward had come home — from Formosa. In his eightieth year and with his hospital in China closed to him, this time by the Communists, he and Georgie had begun a new life on Taiwan. Pleased as newlyweds they kept house in a modern two-room bungalow and each morning — a bent little man with whitest hair, the complexion of an ivory mandarin figurine — Edward propelled himself in a pedaled rickshaw a mile down the road to the huge refugee camp where he conducted a clinic. He was like a boy about this new means of propulsion: no man running his heart out for him, like a beast between the shafts; no need to learn to drive a car! It seemed impossible, however, that he could still work. His back, broken in an accident and improperly mended, had diminished his six-foot stature to a misshapen five-and-a-half; a body which had fought cholera, plague and malaria showed its battles in a waxy pallor and sudden, chill sweats; he was getting deaf. But what counted was as strong as ever: he didn't need glasses and his hands were steady; his faith and sweetness were more sure than ever.

One day he wrote Henry: "I want to come home for a visit and sit with you in the study at 55 and talk, just as we have always done." The letter was forwarded to me and I stared at it as though it came from another world. What about my letter to him, breaking the news of his brother's condition? He had received it; he couldn't have understood it. I wrote again, more explicitly, trying to forestall what seemed a hopeless journey or at least prepare him. I might as well have written to Uranus; I couldn't have been more mistaken.

Twice every day that they were in Hartford the two old people arrived in a taxi from their hotel and, supported by the cabdriver and by big strong Mary, they struggled up the stairs and into the sickroom where the object of their visit was, most often, sound asleep.

When his brother's eyes were open, Edward took out his Bible and read aloud to him. Henry paid no attention. Sometimes there was a little talk between them but Henry usually couldn't understand and Edward seldom heard. On one occasion Henry understood all too well.

Edward had pulled out of his pocket a copy of the Beatitudes, wreathed in roses and forget-me-nots.

"Do you remember, Henry, when our mother taught us these?"

"Taught us what?"

"The Beatitudes."

"Of course I do." (How scathingly he said it! But Edward hadn't heard.)

"Let me read them to you."

Henry sparkled with mischief: "I bet I remember them better than *you* do!"

But Edward went on, unperturbed: "Blessed are the poor in spirit . . ."

"Edward!" the sick man roared, "if you read me that, I warn you, I'm going under the covers!"

"For they shall see God . . ."

Henry was not strong enough to pull the covers over his head, but he tried. "Edward bores me," he complained to me, "always talking about *his* interests."

Once, when Edward said to him on leaving the room, "Next time I see you, Henry. . . ." Henry broke in tartly, "Next time, I hope, you'll be on a slow boat to China."

"What did you say?"

Sooner or later during these visits, one, two or all three of the dear old people fell asleep. The problem was how to steer the two who were up to a couch before they dropped off.

Moving on to New York didn't stop the daily visits to

the sick man. For three weeks more Edward, and often Georgie, too, took the train to Hartford, made their call and took the train back again — a six- or seven-hour journey. Sometimes the visit lasted only a few minutes; it might be at any time of day. Railroad conductors and train crews came to know the little white-haired man with his rubbers and umbrella, books bulging his pockets. It was a frightful nuisance — getting that almost helpless body of his up and down train steps, finding him a seat and getting him into it — "But God dammit," they said to one another, "did you ever see such a sweet guy?"

One evening they came at ten o'clock. "Your brother's just fallen asleep," said the nurse. "I feel terribly but he's had a bad day and I really don't think he should be wakened." But one might as well talk to the sky as to those quiet eyes. "That's all right," Edward reassured her, "I'll just sit." And he sat; praying. The interesting thing was that after these visits Henry was better.

Crazy — absolutely crazy — people said, hearing about it. Marvelous! said others; did you ever hear of anything so wonderful? "What are your plans?" I asked them. "We're going back to Formosa," they said, "that's our home now and the Lord has work for us to do." I murmured something about the hardships of travel, but the Lord, they said, would provide.

And I thought of Mother, standing in a window of the study, looking out at the maples with a sad look. "You know, it's really terrible with poor Edward and Georgie. They have no real home, and they're going to want to come back here someday when they are really old. Henry

should ask them to live here, but I don't believe somehow that he will. And it's so sad — because this is their
home . . ."

But soon it wasn't even Henry's home. The Board of
Education selected Nook Farm as the ideal location for
the new High School and nothing and no one in the en-
suing battle, waged by eleven Forest Street families, by
historical societies, associations of architects and literary
historians — nothing could divert the tide.

So Henry left "55" for the last time, for a nursing home
(where — strangely — the disposition of windows and
doors in the room was almost identical to his own) and a
few weeks later Edward was in the same home, in exactly the same condition as his brother. Having lived their
lives half the world apart, the brothers were to end them
within a few feet of one another, neither knowing the
other was there.

6

How can one's father die? Not be? One's mother, yes, she dies; she comes to an end. But your source? That *is* life: the unknown, continuing mystery. It doesn't really end. By dying it gives birth — not as the mother does, to the child's body, but by releasing into the human stream whatever has still remained fastened: bud to stem, today to yesterday, less to more. One becomes, then, a different child, with no parents and nothing but brothers and sisters. First we are made children physically; for a little time (how very little) we are parents physically; with our parents' deaths we are born as persons spiritually — unattached, unprotected, illegitimate. WHO IS THE FATHER? No one can tell.

I had been asleep.

It's only five (I thought), hardly light yet; I'll try to go back to sleep. But last night — that was so delicious, and funny, and everyone in the room was so marvelous (how much themselves they were, each one!) that I want to stay awake and go over it all again. What was it Lenny said? Why did he make the Game that hard? Only of course I should have recognized the line from Keats: "Nature's patient sleepless eremite" — the words are sleepy, aren't they? All by themselves, they're sleepy. Quiet now, you are dropping off, don't wake yourself up, let yourself . . . I suppose I like parlor games because I was brought up on them. How Daddy would have loved last night!

"Wait, don't let me go till I'm in!"

The boat rocks terribly while I take my place in it.

"Now I'm all right."

There is a tremendous shove, though I don't see who does it, and I shoot off downstream, down a narrow, tumultuous river between banks so high little light comes through. The boat — it isn't very big, is it? not much bigger than I am, but it has plenty of freeboard, thank God for that. I don't like this river I'm on; I don't like the way the water looks: the waves standing up in peaks all around as though it stayed in one place, but the boat, look, it is tearing! We shot some rapids once that were just like this; a boy had drowned in them and they called them after him: "Little Joe" . . . And the cliffs on either side! they must go up two or three hundred feet and I could never climb them they're so steep. Wait — what have I got to steer with? Nothing! Nothing at all!

"Why do you want to steer?" a voice asks from the top of the cliff on the right. There is the silhouette of a very tall figure up there, in the same place the voice comes from. Wind flaps the long robe around its ankles.

"Look at this water!" I shout back. "I have to!"

From the opposite cliff falls another voice: "Where are you going?"

"I don't know. I was just shoved off." More figures gather, on both cliffs — I can't see their faces; they are just dark shapes against the morning sky. Except for their clothes fluttering in the wind (are they all wearing those long robes?) nothing about them moves. They are pure voice.

"Are you afraid?" one calls.

"I guess so, a little."

"Why?"

"Because I'm going so fast, and the boat may tip over; isn't that reason enough?"

"No. Because it isn't the real reason."

I hang my head and see that spray has begun to dash over the gunwale. "No," I shout back, angry now. "You are right! It's because I'm alone!"

"That's a funny one! Everybody is — is — issssssss . . ."

What's the matter with him? Is he stuttering, or laughing? Whatever he's doing, it goes on and on in the strangest, most annoying way.

That isn't laughing, it's ringing. It's the telephone: the instrument is on the shelf, above and to the right, don't you remember? Reach for it — you can find it — stop that ringing . . . stop it.

"Hello?"

"Is this 1164?"

"Yes."

"Go ahead, Hartford." The voice that comes through is the voice of one of the nurses, Mrs. D. — marvelously close and alive and physical.

"I've been trying to get you," she begins, "but I guess the wires were out. My dear, I'm sorry to tell you, but your father just passed away. Yes . . . just a little while ago . . ."

⤴**⤻۞⤴**⤻۞⤴**⤻۞⤴**⤻۞⤴**⤻۞⤴**⤻۞⤴**⤻۞⤴**⤻۞⤴**⤻۞⤴**⤻۞⤴**⤻۞⤴**⤻۞⤴**

PEOPLE die of themselves; houses have to be taken apart
and put to death, and this falls to women to do — to the
same people who make houses live. No wonder they cling
to belongings, doing so not only out of sentiment or ac-
quisitiveness, but in deference to the house itself — as
though to expiate the sacrifice: Forgive me for taking out
your eyes, your heart, but I will care for them, oh so
well . . . It is a pilgrimage, too, all that communing with
what has gone before. And it is a dance: a house being
emptied and closed for the last time, is like a rich and
somber ballet. There are the chief dancers, occupying center stage and disappearing from time to time into the
wings yet always returning, in new combinations, to ex-
ecute new figures. There are the comic (and macabre)
clowns and there is an almost unending succession of
choruses — the dance of the teacups, the chairs, the
spoons; the slow pas-seuls of old letters. On stage, off
stage! That finishes tables; let's bring on the lamps! and

a new group slides in. On and on it goes, to music the heart makes.

And the house makes its own music. Someone winds an old clock, but fails to make it run, and is startled, later, to hear the tiny crystalline voice of its striking; a Chinese temple gong is touched, old records played — and all the time there is the soundless obbligato of things asking to stay, to remain undisturbed, to be left together.

On the top floor — in the half-dark outside the empty maids' rooms, the children discover an old music box: Oh please — can we play it? And for half an hour, while they exclaim over the contents of a closet, the dusty third-floor chill reverberates and tinkles to "Carnaval de Venise," the "Wedding March," "The Last Rose of Summer." From the closet come girls' voices: "Look, a helmet, of chain mail! And a big bird of brass, with an egg for its body!" "What kind of egg is that big?" "It's an ostrich egg! And look, it opens and is lined with red velvet." "Here's a sword, and goodness . . . fans, and tortoise-shell combs . . . how do I look?" "You should have a mantilla."

The closet ravished, they go on to the attic, their mother leading the way with a light on a long cord — past a funny old varnished brown crib ("Whoever slept in *that* thing?") past piled-up trunks, a tangle of ice axes and mountain-eer's ropes, a guitar, to the closet where — oh delicious horror — hangs a real skeleton. Can we unwrap it? And the bones of fingers go on swinging after being let drop, and out in the hall, more dimly from here, sounds the waltz from *Rigoletto*, its deep melodious bass too un-broken, too regular, delicately touched and plucked by the

little plink! of the doves. It is the voice of the house, singing.

Hungrily, absorbed, the two girls go from room to room,
looking, picking up and putting down, choosing what they
would like to keep for their own. The older one wanted
art books. I find her sitting cross-legged on the floor, like
a Buddha, turning the pages of an album on Michelangelo.
"Look, Mummy, what fell out . . ." and she hands me
two little watercolors of Venice: Santa Maria della Salute,
with its white scrolls; the red shaft of San Giorgio. "Who
did these, do you know?"

"What on earth's *this?*" asks the younger one, bringing
us a square wooden box with a handle sticking out from it.
"Wind it," says her sister, but nothing happens. Their
father and I have a look, and shake the box, then he pulls
out a little button and a nightingale sings, pauses, sings
again. The whole house rings with its rhapsodies — all
those tender experiments starting sometimes with low,
throaty jug-a-jugs, climbing into breathless little exclama-
tions — like the wood thrush's improvisations but more
passionate, and here, in one's hands.

The house that day was particularly full of life. The
girls were everywhere, become all eyes and hands and ears
— their sensibilities as finely avid as the tiny feathery
graspings of feeding limpets. In the study, their uncle
sorted papers, bringing them to me to review together and
feed what was not for keeping to the fire in our parents'
bedroom. All day the fire burned — roaring up alarmingly
if we fed it too fast, building stiff layers of blackened
debris, coating the brasses with dark iridescence. What

do we do with *these?* What are they? Diplomas, de-grees. What does one do, if they are not to collect unseen in other lockers, other attics? But they die hard. The sheepskin writhed and twisted and tossed, bending almost double, straightening out again with terrible jerks.

Following close in all our wakes went Mary, carrying ob-jects, carrying messages, her eyes alight with adventure, chin trembling with tears. In the kitchen meals were pre-pared and served. Way off in a corner of the cellar, my husband sorted wines, opening and sniffing questionable vintages, packing or throwing out. Overhead there was walking to and fro, and — very far off — the nightingale's spasmodic singing. Down here it was so quiet his shoes on the cement scraped the bottom of silence; silence cir-cled away down the drain in the glug-glugs of poured-off wine.

That night, as on many nights, I was left alone in the house with the maids, and the others' departures for the everyday world of the living set whirlpools spinning. "Those are *my* things there; could you, possibly, add them to my books?" "Have someone throw out the last bottles — they're vinegar." "There's a strong smell of smoke in the attic; I'd have a look if I were you."

When they had all gone, I went to the attic. Had we overstuffed the fire? Started something in the chimney? The smell was terribly strong, but the wall was cool to touch and the air in the beam of the light I carried was clear. Standing there in the immense, chilly quiet, among the old trunks and bedsprings, my baby crib, my grand-mother's guitar, I felt the whole gravitational pull of the house and its contents under my feet. It was an entire world, made up of thousands of lesser worlds, I was tearing apart. Supposing it burned to the ground tonight, and I with it? Life plays just such tricks. You're overwrought, I told myself; and slept as if already dead.

Three different times Betsy came, and worked with me from morning till late night, diving into the dirtiest, dullest places, spurring me to decisions when I flagged with confusion. How can you bear to do it, I asked her, looking at her blackened fingers, the circles under eyes that were bright with interest: one's own house, perhaps, but someone else's? She couldn't explain. But one saw some gravity drawing her too, and together we worked in the same kind of humming harmony with which we had once written behind the piano.

What things came to light! What things had been saved, as though one might have to start life over again from nothing yet still wearing lace and real silk and traveling with top hats in leather hatboxes! We even found the slippery black skin off a man's silk hat, neatly rolled into a bundle and marked.

"What's in this closet?" asked Betsy, pulling open a door.

"The electric closet?"

"The *what?*"

"It's what it was always called."

The only reason for this we could discover was a supply of light bulbs and two beat-up old electric fans; the rest of the closet was stuffed with travel paraphernalia: folding spirit lamps, padded bottle cases, traveling flasks and bookbags, a flaccid old writing case and an odd tangle of tapes and pouches which was utterly mystifying. Betsy turned it and twisted it, this way and that, her head on one side. "It's a money belt!" we both said at once.

Sometimes, from the thousands and thousands of things that underwent scrutiny or at least passed under our eyes, single objects spoke — like the two lace baby bonnets marked Edward and Henry; like the white flannel petticoat, dark yellow now, which had a little note pinned to it: "Worn by Mary Evelyn Dwight on the day of her wedding; wrapped around Henry A. Perkins at his christening."

Sometimes odd forces seemed to work with us, as when I laid my hand — in the dark — on an unopened package of French glass prisms — identical in design, and number, to those the painters had just broken in Betsy's chandelier.

And sometimes doors opened right into a life as in the letter found in one of the study lockers. ("I can't open this one!" Betsy complained, wrestling with the lock. "Here — I know about that: the key is bent.") The letter, still fresh and white, was to "dear Mary." "Since you were my very first girl" (it read) "I must write you now to confess that it was very hard for me to accept your marriage — so hard that only now have I finally become reconciled, and this because I, too, am about to be married. Her name is Josepha . . ." The letter was signed Edward.

"Oh dear, who were they, do you suppose?" Betsy turned it over and over in her hand, the paper crackling in the silence of the richly inhabited room. Mary: that was Mary

Evelyn. And Edward? Of course, he was one of the children she was engaged to tutor — years younger than the gay little postmistress he loved who was his first, most idolized girl.

Often we worked until very late at night, made dizzy and maudlin by the sheer number of things. Seventy-two Limoges teacups — of one pattern; forty-eight of others! Thirty white damask tablecloths, small mountains of lace doilies. All the time Mary hovered about us, bringing us morning coffee in bed, begging us to take naps, and each night serving us dinner in the big dining room, by candle-light, where we sat watched from over the mantel by a Murillo fruit vender, luscious as the ripe grapes in the basket on her hip, from over the sideboard by a vinegary ancestress in a starched cap. Between us and the pantry door a rip in the Chinese screen made the murdering hawk swing with each swing of the door. So far, life had not left the house at all: its reason was gone, but its contents were more alive than ever. "How can you?" I kept asking Betsy. "It's no ordinary house," she replied.

But the real journey must be made alone. It is through a world without time. This picture of my mother, buried among father's ties (in a tie-case I had embroidered with iris) must have been taken when she first came to this country: she is younger here than our eldest daughter — tiny-waisted, a little wistful, vivid as she always was. And here is her schoolbag with its little flask for ink, and her atlas, all in Danish, with some of the pages shockingly scribbled on. (So you scribbled too, and someone scolded you . . .)

And this picture of a young man, signed Alfred Flinch across the bottom: it is his reporter's pass to the Paris Exposition of '78. So that's what you looked like in your thirties, Grandfather. Grandfather! How ridiculous: grandfathers are old men! And look at you — so young and with your head at an angle that is daring the whole world to stop you. I know what you are going to look like when you're seventy (after all those things you have to live through, too!); I have that picture of you as well, wearing the little scholar's cap, your eyelids heavy with knowledge and one with a fold in it like that of a caged bird in too bright light.

And here is Grandmother's party list: a notebook with hundreds of names in alphabetical order all checked off in blue or red crayon and — on the flyleaf — this note: "Blue-marked to be considered. Not the red." What had the poor red done? Suddenly Grandmother, in her black bottle dress, at the head of the white damask table, steps out of her own larger-than-life figure and approaches me with that gurgling laugh — artificial, gallant little snob that she must have been.

Most of Father's past was in the study: like an archeologist assembling scraps and shards I have pieced together what I could of his career. His dressing room was like a portrait sketch — delicately colored as those drawings of the dead the Egyptians laid outside a mummy's wrapping. Here, among piles of monogrammed shirts, vests of fawn suede cloth and evening brocade, I found his flute, his musette, his flageolet: "my whistles." On top of the chiffonier, between a jewel case and a bottle of toilet water, an Indian box disclosed a tatting shuttle and several yards of tatting.

And then there are his actual pictures — all the photographs of him. Does every generation look back from under its own burden at the one preceding it, thinking: How young you were, my parents, how much easier it must have been, then, to juggle life's pressures? I look not only at my father's face when young, but also at the group photographs — of picnics, reunions, shipboard acquaintances — and their gay confidence, their unselfconscious playfulness, the boys' arms around one another's waists, dates them more surely than the high collars and tapering trouser legs. Our new awarenesses have opened canyons between us and their generation wider than can ever be measured by years, or wars, or new inventions. For better or worse, and with no more wisdom to meet it than they had, our common unconscious has been disclosed to us; the guilt of possession implanted in us; the awe-fulness of the universe shown to us.

And my mother? A woman's life is played, like music; you can't play it back. And she — even when she was most alive, in fact, particularly then — was a spirit not quite at home on earth and not wholly one of us. She tried to be, but it was like her languages: she spoke each one she knew so perfectly, with such respect and feeling for the fine nuances of communication, that in France she was assumed to be French, in Germany, German, in this country, American. Only one thing puzzled those interested enough to speculate about her "accent": she must come (they said) from some other part of their country.

Some other part! Another place! This was her greatness and her tragedy; for in that "other place" things were not so miserably human, disappointing, sad: you didn't have to battle for each least vision vouchsafed to you; you *were* your vision.

Maybe this is why the little substance she did leave behind seems so strangely unreal, so little a part of her. Aside from her clothes, the boxes of recipes and letters, the notebooks begun and abandoned (how hard she tried to be systematic, how little she was!) all that is left of her past is in the little glass-front bookcase full of Danish and philosophical works. Two drawers at the bottom contain her notebooks on the theatre arts — completed, the notes in a firm, round hand; part of the costume she had worn in her first part; a letter from the great Mrs. Lemoine: "Dear Olga, I was in the audience last night at your production of the Prince and the Pauper . . . no one knows better than I what goes into anything so perfect . . ." And, among the albums, a bottle full of shells, as small and white as first teeth, a photograph of Will Gillette (so worldly! so breathtakingly handsome!) and a little album of photographs of Mount Desert, in Maine: one from a mountaintop, with windblown blueberry bushes in the foreground and a light-struck view of distant islands: someone let the sun shine into the lens.

Time has lost all meaning; relationships dissolve. The idea of "parents," and "grandparents" falls off like a fairytale vanishing act. These are people just like me — some older, or younger, more confident or more lost, congenial or not — and all of us connected — not, as I used to think, by our same blood but by our same end. Selecting what to keep out of what was theirs, I prepare for my own death and for the similar journey my children will make after me. We are all in the same, fluid element.

It is like walking undersea. I peer this way and that, enter caves full of treasure where, absorbed and bemused, I pick up, examine, put down. Past many kinds of dim scenery I move steadily, slowly or fast, but always move. Figures move past; sometimes an evil face looks out from a cranny. If I stay submerged too long I tire, go vaguely doing unnecessary things; I must surface for a while into the blinding, dazzling, deafening world of the living.

Where does it lead? What am I looking for? Myself. The tiny point in time and place, and in this strangely rich pattern, which is "me." I am a convergence of all these personalities, emotions, events — in the frame of these thousands of things from all over the world. I am, myself, a small world that happened out of a thousand worlds.

The real taking apart began; the worlds were scattered. "Something is going which you just don't find any more today," said my older daughter sadly. "Shame, nice house like this," said Jo, the night freight handler.

Next door, in the Warner house, where they were getting ready to move out, too, the little redheaded boy and his round sister covered the walls of a third-floor room with crayoned protests. "Pleese, don't tare us down!" issued from the mouths of belligerent people with outspread fingers and hair on end. "I'll *shoot* you if you take us down!" was scrawled around the muzzle of a gun. "You are being watched," said a huge eye staring from the ceiling right inside the door. In the next room their mother, a lock of hair along her cheek, was packing, packing: the quartet would be playing tonight, she must finish this one pile.

The night before the movers came, I sat in our living room — still whole and untouched except for a tag here, a label there, looking about a last time at that gentle, kindly space with its gold-colored walls like suede to touch, its brown velvet curtains drawn as usual, the lamps lit. They still made only small pools of light. To read you had to draw up your chair. In the soft dimness all sorts of things lit up: gilt frames and porcelain shoulders of vases, leather bindings, the proud, satin-covered breast and curl-framed forehead of our ancestress Mabel Harlakenden. I looked at the wing chair where my mother always sat and from where she poured tea. This was her room: her presence still warmed and illuminated it. And she had been as well the impresario who had selected — from how many arts and tastes and crafts! — combining her choices into this lovely whole. "What will I do with that horrible table?" I could hear her asking, answering her own question with the beautiful Chinese embroidery she placed on its top, the chair she put beside it. Wasn't this her monument (as it is so many women's) — this giving a house, or a room, life? A little of it I would keep, but most of it was going — "out of the world," my child had said. The flood was engulfing eleven families but where the others were moving to higher land and taking their treasures with them, I was throwing out what was fast disappearing from all over the earth: the things that take time, and concern, to make; that have no purpose at all but to give pleasure.

The books went last. As the rooms emptied and began to reverberate to footsteps and hammering of crates, they still lined the walls, beautifully rich and contained and undemanding. In what house would they ever stand again together like this — Voltaire and Racine and Corneille? The Italian poets? Goethe and Schiller and Lessing? Ibsen and Strindberg? I wanted to ask someone's forgiveness, but whether it was the authors' or my ancestors' or my descendants' I could not tell. The world had changed, that was all, and reading what the great and the perceptive said about it, in their own tongues, was now about as important as knowing how to fence. Then finally they went, too — the thousands of books — and the auction was held, and then the house really *was* dead except for a small pile of debris in each room, and in the front hall a trunk full of costumes, and on a mantel upstairs, bunches and bunches of keys.

The city's plans took longer than expected. Until the following spring the eleven houses stood empty, blind-eyed in the winter quiet, dead leaves knee-deep in their corners. Here and there a window was broken and vandals ripped out a cupboard or a fixture; on the front porch of "55" a long-handled, tattered parasol rolled around by itself in the wind for weeks before it disappeared. In and out among the great old trees the blue jays skimmed — sharp thrusts of blue, voicing their harsh cries. And everywhere there were hundreds of squirrels, the fattest in generations, flicking undisturbed among their unimaginable wealth of hiding places for nuts.

With the first crocuses the wrecking cranes appeared, the destruction began. Iron teeth chewed off whole rooms at a bite — crunched into a bedroom here, a conservatory there; with horrible dexterity the searching mouths, swinging on their long dinosaur necks, spat copper gutters into one pile, doors in another, tenderly lipped glass and windows into waiting trucks. The brick and plaster and lath that weren't worth saving was let fall with a horrifying crash that sent clouds of ashy dust up into the trees. Between fresh crashes one heard the continuing rattle of falling masonry and the cloud never settled — it only thickened. Ahead of the cranes, the doomed houses waited their turn, being stripped, vomiting beams from their open windows. It was like war.

But unlike war, the rubble rapidly and completely vanished as bulldozers filled in cellar holes and trucks carted away till nothing belonging to a house — not a shingle, or crumb of mortar, or loop of wire — was left behind. Only the trees still stood, majestic and untouched, in their new leaves. And the grass crept up over the house sites — grass, then flowering weeds, which grew as high as where floors had been and feet once walked. People going through the street on their way to the factories or the shops on the avenue looked, amazed and not quite sure of what they saw. For it *was* a forest now: a forest of monumental trees, with here and there a small clearing (and how small the clearings looked!), into which sun slanted and one would not have been too startled to come upon a deer. Houses? Had there ever been houses? Let's see: that must be the oak in front of the Perkins house, and there was a grove of cedars to the cast — so the house was placed here, wasn't it? — but how was there room for it in that little space? I don't think it could have been there . . . I must be mistaken. And the grass grew till it was waist-high and squeaky with juice, and plunk in the middle of what had once been the lawn of "55," four little girls, one day in July, had a woods picnic. From the street, when they sat down to eat their sandwiches and popsicles, they couldn't be seen at all . . .

Long before this, of course, the trunkful of costumes had gone to the boys' school on the other side of the mountain, and in a laboratory of the same school the skeleton was hung. Almost every day, now, some boy picks up the fingers and lets them drop, opens and closes the jaws, pokes his own inquisitive fingers into the empty eyesockets. A. P. Yorick they call him.

And in Mark Twain's house the bottle-green stair carpet, which used to be the pathway to the Magic Closet, leads up the wide stairs to his study and on to the children's schoolroom. But most wonderful of all — the old music box with the silver doves stands right in the front hall and when it starts playing, the whole huge stairwell — straight up to the far-off skylight — reverberates and tinkles with its music.

Epilogue

THERE REMAINED the ring. How can anyone else possess or wear one's mother's wedding ring? That, or the gold brooch given on a golden wedding anniversary? I had intended them to go with her, but they had been forgotten. There was only one destination for them and that was the sea, where she herself had wanted to end.

When we went for a week's sail, that summer, I had them with me, waiting for the proper time and place to submit them. On a quiet, blue day it came. The wind had lightened and we barely moved, with softest lappings, through the water. Blue was everywhere — sustaining us, arching over us, and land itself nothing but the palest blue, its end marked by the white exclamation point of a lighthouse. I went out in the bow, alone, the jewels in my pocket, and was overtaken by a fearful reluctance to do what I was going to do. Should I wear the pin, perhaps? Keep that? No. Father had given it to her, as a token of their fifty years; it wasn't mine. Should I keep the ring?

Why? For what? Who would ever care, or look at it? I pulled it out of my pocket and studied it and instantly it brought before me the memory of mother's hand wearing the ring — of the glint of it all through my childhood, the feeling of it against my cheek or knee or hand as she touched me. I saw it in lamplight as she sewed; against her face as she leaned on an elbow, writing; flickering in and out of her hair as she brushed it. Since before I'd been born she had worn this; it had encircled a part of her. As she lay in the coffin it had rested against her waist. I looked at it more closely. The outer surface was dull with scratches; where it had lain against skin it was worn to a fiery, mirror smoothness. Something was written inside: initials, and the date of the wedding. I held it inside my closed palm as though closing my hand over her.

I threw the pin first. It sparkled briefly and swept away under the bow and for a dreadful instant I wondered if it would catch in the log line streaming away astern and what the others would say, finding it.

Then I opened my hand to throw the ring — ring that had held what delights and what despairs no one else would know — that was all that was left, now, of my parents' marriage, the union which had made me, which had urged me all those years to redeem a little the unhappiness it brought them — first by cherishing and trying to console her, then — when she had gone — by making it up to him. Child, rushing in where angels create and destroy!

"In heaven there is neither giving or taking in marriage." Yet we are the children of a marriage as well as of two people. Do we all try to dissolve that connection of which we are the result? Break its hold upon us so that we may be related by love alone to each beloved parent? Doing so, we start the antithesis from which *our* children rebel, who then swing another curve of the circle. It is indeed a ring in which we are circled, which we polish with our selves, which life abrades.

I let it go, into the sea. It shone as it circled downward through translucent green. It disappeared, and as it did so I lay, face down on the deck, as drained as if blood had flowed out of me in a stream. The bow whispered through the water: I took a deep breath. As I exhaled, with some sort of huge acceptance and relief, a gust blew the water dark blue and the boat leaped forward, heeling far over. The gust grew into a wind, driving us ahead, hard, taut, singing.